Schools Council

Open Science

Leon Darrall

Teachers' Guide

WITHDRAWN

Published for the Schools Council
by Hart-Davis Educational and Hutchinson

Published jointly by Hart-Davis Educational
Frogmore, St Albans, Hertfordshire
and Hutchinson & Co (Publishers) Ltd
24 Highbury Crescent, London N5.

First published 1980

ISBN 0 247 12914 3

Designed and produced by Logos Design

Illustrations by: Illustra Design, Positif-Press,
Rodney Paull.

Printed in Great Britain by The Anchor Press Ltd

All orders and sales enquiries
to Hart-Davis Educational

Contents

Schools Council Science for the Less Able Pupil Project

Background

The extension of the school leaving age to 16 and the reorganisation of the majority of secondary schools under a comprehensive plan meant for some schools changes in school curriculum, for some teachers changes in teaching styles and for many pupils an extra year at school. To assist in the implementation of these changes, so far as science teaching was concerned, a team of science teachers was set up to produce suitable science material to meet the needs of pupils between the ages of 14-16 years whose performances, academically, have been regarded in the lower band of achievement.

The writers were all teachers chosen for their wide experience in teaching those pupils who would generally be classified as least able.

The project was funded by Schools Council as one of the first locally based curriculum development projects. Help and encouragement was also given by the Birmingham Education Department. The team was allowed two years to produce the material which included extensive testing of the trial material in 30 local secondary schools.

Project objectives

1. To produce science material for secondary school pupils having regard to both their educational development and to their chronological age.
2. The materials produced to have an interest value suitable for pupils, between the ages of 14-16 years, whose performances academically, have been in the lower band of achievement.
3. To produce a workable programme of science related topics which teachers could use in their science lessons, particularly, with pupils who have limited powers of concentration, a restrictive vocabulary and possibly language problems generally.
4. To suggest ideas which introduce new skills for pupils with low motivation and at the same time endeavouring to extend their educational and scientific experiences
5. The content of the material produced to have a variety of themes, but to remain relevant to the pupils' needs and interests.

Design and structure of the project

There are 13 Pupil Units each of 32 pages, this Teachers' Guide and a set of Record Sheet Masters.

Pupils' Units

The units are completely independent of each other and no progression, as such, has been built into them except where a series of activities follow some logical sequence. The language in the units has been carefully controlled to minimise reading problems. The target reading age of the material was 9 years. The layout is clear with large type for easy comprehension. The illustrations are simple, yet designed to be visually appealing to pupils of this age range and at the same time providing visual clues to help understanding. The units are activity based and emphasis has been placed on 'learning by doing'. In most cases the layout has been designed in such a way that one activity covers a double page and the subject matter deals with basic materials which relate to the underlying concepts that science is relevant to and part of everyday living.

Very few assumptions have been made about the pupils' previous scientific experiences or about their knowledge of scientific concepts and principles. It has been assumed, however, that pupils will have sufficient skills in the processes of science to enable them to observe, to classify, to record, to count, to manipulate simple apparatus, to measure, to draw and copy diagrams, to work individually and in groups and to follow simple instructions. It has also been assumed that pupils will have a reading age of 10/11 years.

Every activity in each of the Units follows a similar pattern in design. It tells the pupils 'What they will need', 'What to do', 'Where to record their results' followed by questions based on that activity. Where necessary the instructions are supplemented with adequate illustrations.

Teachers' Guide

For the teacher this Guide gives practical classroom advice on the teaching of each activity. For the laboratory technician there are comprehensive lists of apparatus and detailed drawings showing how to construct the apparatus needed for some activities in certain units.

Record Sheet Masters

These are printed sheets of all the record tables, charts and questions which can be reproduced by teachers for distribution to their pupils if work in exercise books is preferred to direct recording in the Unit. Since these masters will be in a printed form the reprographic method used can be freely chosen, but obviously will depend upon the facilities available in any one particular school.

Using the Units

The Units have been designed for use in two distinct ways. (1) As normal class books with pupils using them in combination with their science exercise books or, (2) as workbooks in which the pupils are able to make immediate recordings as they work through the Activities in the Units. There has been no rigid sequence built into the Units and they can, therefore, be used independently of each other in any order which the teacher wishes. Alternatively, the Units can be linked to provide sufficient material for particular topics e.g. for a topic on 'Safety' the following Units could be used: Fire — Safe Eating — Electricity in the Home — Science at Home. Or, for a topic on the Environment the following may be found useful: Pollution — Life Spotting — Grow Your Own. Some schools include in their science schemes work based on the motor car. Such schools might find the following Units useful: Find Out About Machines — Machines On The Move — Starting and Stopping - Keeping Going. In other words, there is a flexibility built into the Units which will allow teachers to use the course in the way that best suits the ability of their pupils and their particular resources. In this way, it is possible for the material to supplement or complement teachers'own schemes of work.

CSE MODE 3

It is possible to use Open Science materials as the basis for a Mode 3 CSE examination. A number of schools are developing schemes for CSE Examining Boards. For example, the West Midlands Examinations Board has approved a Mode 3 exam based on Open Science (taken by pupils in six schools in Birmingham). A paper giving further information and guidance on running such schemes is available from the publishers. It gives examples of syllabuses, assessment arrangements and examination questions. It may also be possible to put interested teachers in touch with groups of schools currently running such CSE Mode 3 schemes should more detailed information be needed.

Electricity in the Home

Summary of contents

The first Activity in the Unit investigates the meaning of the data given on the information plates of electrical appliances, such as volts, amps, serial number, watts, H.P., cycles, etc. The appliances are first ordered according to wattage and then regrouped according to the function they perform, e.g. lighting, heating, mechanical, or an aid to communications.

The cost of using electricity is next considered, but at the same time, the mathematical skills needed to perform the calculations are kept as simple as possible.

The dangers caused by overloading electrical circuits are stressed by using a low voltage fused circuit board. The need to earth electrical appliances is also vividly demonstrated by using the 3 pin plug earthing board. Pupils are left in no doubt of the possible dangers and safety hazards caused when a fault occurs in an electrical appliance which is not properly earthed.

House wiring is mentioned and the advantages of ring main circuits are clearly demonstrated using the models suggested.

At the end of the unit a simple check-up is included based on a series of drawings entitled *Looking for danger* in a bathroom, a living room and a bedroom.

Equipment list for whole of Unit

To be made
Domestic electricity meter apparatus
    (Activities 2 and 3)
Model electric fire (Activity 5)
Conductor-insulator testing board (Activity 6)
Circuit overload board (Activity 8)
Board with metal grips (Activity 9)
Earthing board with model man, complete
    with leads (Activity 10)

Ring main circuit board (Activity 11)
Model of ring main (Activity 11)
3.5 V lamp in holder with bare copper wires
    (Activity 11)

To be bought or obtained from other departments
Electricity meter
Sockets to accept 3 pin fused plugs
Various pieces of wood (chipboard,
    blockboard, hardboard, stripwood) for
    baseboards and supports
Small sheet of tinned plate or aluminium
    sheet
Brass terminals (screw type) or nuts and bolts
    (size 2BA)
Spade terminals
Lamps (12 V, 24 W bayonet type; 12 V, 5 W
    M.E.S.)
Lamp holders (bayonet)
Copper tube (Type used for central heating)
Microammeter
Fused switch (Ring mains circuit board)
Cable (as used in domestic ring mains wiring)

To be collected
General electrical appliances covering a range
    of wattages
Variety of items for testing (Activity 6), e.g.
    different kinds of metal, wood, plastic,
    porcelain, cotton, carbon

Assumed normally available in laboratory
Stop watch or stop clock
Graph paper
Low voltage units
Ammeters (10 A)
4 mm leads
3 pin fused plugs
Various sizes of screwdrivers
Pliers
Wire strippers

3 core cable
Fuse wire (5 A) *or* bare copper wire
  (S.W.G. 36)
4½ V battery
3 A cartridge fuses

Nichrome wire (S.W.G. 26)
4 mm sockets and plugs
Extra flexible insulated wire
Lamp holders (M.E.S. type)
Bare copper wire (S.W.G. 18 and S.W.G. 22)

Forward planner

Activity number	Advanced planning needed	Approximate Activity time (40 min period)	Are results of a previous Activity necessary?
1	Collect a variety of electrical appliances with a range of wattages	2 periods	No
2	*	1 period	Activity 1
3	*	2 periods	No
4	Collection of old electricity bills useful (class Activity)	2 periods	Activities 1-3 can be referred to
5	None *	2 periods	No
6	Collect items to test for insulators and conductors *	1 period	No
7	None	2 periods	No
8	None *	1 period	No
9	None *	1 period	No
10	None (teacher demonstration) *	2 periods	Activity 9 can be referred to
11	None *	2 periods	Activity 9 can be referred to
12	None (class Activity)	1 period	Activities 6, 8, 9, 10

It is necessary to talk through the whole unit with the class before work begins.
* Assumes that apparatus for these Activities has already been made.

Notes for teacher

Activities 1-3
These Activities introduce pupils to the electrical terms commonly used when discussing electrical appliances, e.g. volts (voltage), amps (amperage), watts (wattage). It is hoped that they will ultimately understand the relationship between these units of measurement after the practical work has been carried out:
Power (in watts) = Current (in amps) × Voltage (in volts)

    Although pupils will have had experience of reading dials it is also important that they are aware that the meter measures the energy consumed and that this varies with the power of the apparatus used. Some pupils may need help with the construction of the graph.

Activity 4
Paying for electricity always introduces the use of mathematical processes, simple though they may be, and this tends to cause pupils to lose interest. However, the computations have been kept to a minimum. It can be made more relevant if the pupils bring household electricity bills to school and discussions centre around how it may be possible to economise on the use of electricity around the home.

Activity 5
In the work on the heating effect of the electric current, teachers should also introduce the unintentional heating effect produced in electric cables, leading to the need for fuses.

Activity 6
It may be useful to mount several kinds of insulated wires and cables on a board for general display. This would be useful as a discussion point.

Activity 7
This kind of Activity is very often overlooked, in the sense that it is simple or it is assumed that most people know how to do it. Obviously fuse values must be discussed since they depend upon the appliance to which the plug is to be attached (3 A for appliances of 700 W or less, 13 A between 700 W and 3 kW). As an added exercise, pupils could be asked to devise a simple 'fuse tester' to check if a fuse has 'blown'. (See Activity 10.)

At this stage it might be useful to develop the idea of short circuits and discuss how these occur and what can be done to help prevent them taking place. A spectacular *teacher demonstration* can be done by connecting fuse wire across terminals on a board and then connecting these to a mains supply via a fused plug (see diagram below). The fuse wire will melt with a bang and a shower of sparks; it is therefore important that pupils should be moved to a safe distance away and that a safety screen is used.

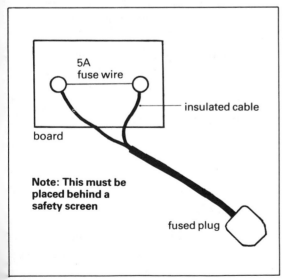

Note: This must be placed behind a safety screen

Setup for the teacher demonstration of short circuits.

Activity 8
Overloading electric circuits can be dangerous. The Activity is straightforward but a check on the use of the correct fuse wire is important. Ordinary bare copper wire (S.W.G. 36) can be used if 5 A wire does not melt.

Activity 9
A simple but necessary Activity. A centre reading microammeter (rather than a milliammeter) should give adequate results.

Activity 10
This is an important Activity since it demonstrates vividly the reason electrical appliances should be earthed. Although this is intended as a teacher demonstration it could be used as part of a circus of experiments, provided that pupils thoroughly understand the procedures and skills involved. As well as using the three 4 mm leads, a model fused plug could be used to make it appear more realistic (see diagram 6, page 21) but this would have to be done as a teacher demonstration since the blowing of cartridge fuses could make this an expensive Activity.

Activity 11
Since ring main circuits are now used in most households it is important that pupils understand what they do.

The electricity supply is brought to most homes by underground cables. See diagram 1, page 18, for a simplified circuit.

The service cable consists of two wires called the live (L) and neutral (N), and when it enters the house from the street it is connected first to the electricity board's sealed fuse then through the meter to a consumer unit (fuse box) containing the main switch and fuses for the various circuits. Power circuits (e.g. immersion heaters, cookers) are kept separate from lighting circuits. In the ring main circuit supplying power points, the live and neutral wires each run in two complete rings all the way round the house. In the ring main even if only one point is in use there is current in the whole ring. No wires are idle and so better use is made of them. The chief advantages of a ring circuit over a radial circuit should be stressed: (1) less electric cable is needed for several socket outlets; (2) additional sockets can be fitted anywhere in the ring without the high cost of taking additional wires back to the fuse box.

Activity 12
Since many accidents occur in the home due to faulty wiring, faulty connections or overloading circuits, discussion time should be allowed so that the meaning of this exercise is thoroughly understood.

Main objectives and ideas

Main objectives
1. An awareness and an appreciation of the terms voltage, amperage, wattage
2. A knowledge of how the wattage of an electrical appliance is related to the cost of using it
3. An understanding of the causes and consequences of overloading an electrical circuit
4. Recognition of the safety aspect of earthing electrical appliances
5. Knowledge of modern methods of house wiring

Key ideas
1. Electrical appliances have a range of wattages and therefore need to have fuses of different values in the circuit
2. The cost of using an electrical appliance is related to its wattage
3. The amount of heat given out by an electric fire and the current used depends upon the way the elements in the fire are connected
4. The human body can act as a conductor of electricity
5. The meaning and consequent dangers of overloading an electrical circuit
6. The meaning of 'short circuit' and the value of earthing an electrical appliance
7. Ring main circuits: why they are used

Information for each Activity

Activity 1:
Looking at information plates

Objective
Awareness that different electrical appliances can have different wattages

Experience
Looking at information plates and grouping appliances according to (a) their wattage and (b) their function

Skills involved
1. Ability to identify an information plate
2. Observation and correct recording
3. Ability to recognise the function of an electrical appliance

Unfamiliar words
Appliance, watt, kilowatt, information plate

Safety points
Make sure that pupils switch off and remove plug before examining the information plate.

General notes
Some help may be needed in converting kilowatts to watts (column E) and also with Table 3.

Apparatus list
General electrical appliances found in the home and school

Details for any construction
None

Activity 2:
Domestic electricity meter

Objective
A knowledge of how to read an electricity supply meter by observing the rotating disc

Experience
Using an electricity supply meter with various appliances and observing the rotating disc

Skills involved
1. Plugging in and switching on the appliance/meter circuit
2. Observing and recording movement of the disc

Unfamiliar words
Domestic, least

Safety points
Make sure that all electrical connections (e.g. wires in plugs) are wired in correctly and are safe.

General notes
Some discussion may be necessary on how to rate 'slow', 'medium' and 'fast'.

Apparatus list
Mounted domestic electricity meter
Selection of appliances (see Activity 1)

Details for any construction
See diagram 2, page 19 , for construction of the mount for the electricity meter.

Activity 3:
Using a domestic electricity meter

Objective
A knowledge of how to read an electricity supply meter by observing the rotating disc

Experiences
Using an electricity supply meter with various appliances and calculating the average turns per minute of the rotating disc

Skills involved
1. Plugging in and switching on the appliance/meter circuit
2. Observing and recording movement of the disc
3. Constructing a graph from the results
4. Interpreting the graph drawn

Unfamiliar words
Selection, revolution, graph

Safety points
As for Activity 2, but also (a) if an electric kettle is used, make sure the spout is pointing away from where pupils are working; (b) if fires are used, again make sure there is no safety hazard.

General notes
Many pupils may need help with the construction of the graph and its interpretation

Apparatus list
Mounted domestic electricity meter
Stop watch
Selection of appliances (see Activity 1)
Graph paper

Details for any construction
See diagram 2, page 19, for construction of the mount for the electricity meter.

Activity 4:
Paying for electricity

Objective
To calculate the cost of using various electrical appliances

Experience
Estimating the recurring costs of using general household appliances

Skills involved
1. Some simple mathematical skills
2. Ability to record and group electrical items according to given criteria

Unfamiliar words
Units of electricity, energy, power

Safety points
None

General notes
1. Most of the help pupils will need with this Activity will be with the arithmetic.
2. Discussion on how to save energy in the home would be appropriate.

Apparatus list
No apparatus — a collection of old electricity bills would be useful

Details for any construction
None

Activity 5:
Using electricity for heating

Objective
Awareness that the elements in an electric fire can be connected, by switching, to give varying amounts of heat

Experience
Using a model electric fire to investigate the relationship between the way the elements are wired together and the heat given out

Skills involved
1. Ability to interpret a wiring diagram
2. Ability to read an ammeter
3. Careful observation and recording

Unfamiliar words
Ammeter, circuit, diagram, series, parallel, current

Safety points
Although this is a model fire, working on a 12 V supply, the 'elements' will get very hot; pupils should be warned about this.

General notes
Since the fire has to be wired in three ways, some teacher intervention may be necessary. Some discussion will also be needed when considering the results obtained.

Apparatus list
Model electric fire
12 V supply
Ammeter (0 – 10 A)
3 long
2 short } connecting wires with 4 mm plugs

Details for any construction
See diagram 3, page 19, for construction of the model electric fire.

Activity 6:
Conductors and insulators

Objective
Appreciation that only certain materials will conduct electricity

Experiences
Testing various materials and grouping these into conductors and insulators according to given criteria

Skills involved
1. Recognition of items used
2. Observing and recording

Unfamiliar words
Aluminium, P.V.C., porcelain, conductor, insulator, opposite, cable

Safety points
None

General notes
There should be no difficulty in completing the table of results, but discussion will be necessary before answering the questions.

Apparatus list
Model conductor-insulator testing board
Materials for testing (e.g. several different metals, plastics, cotton, porcelain, wood, rubber)

Details for any construction
See diagram in pupils' book, page 18, for construction of the model conductor-insulator testing board. The exact dimensions are not important but a suggested size for the board is 8 cm by 15 cm, and 1.5 cm thick. The battery can be held in a terry clip approximately 23 mm in diameter.

Activity 7:
Wiring a fused plug

Objective
Understanding the techniques involved in wiring a fused plug

Experiences
Wiring various types of fused plugs and inserting correct fuse

Skills involved
1. Preparing cable for inserting into plug
2. Putting correct wires to appropriate terminals (brown, L; blue, N; green/yellow, E)
3. Checking correct value of fuse

Unfamiliar words
Sockets, cartridge fuse, neutral, terminals, connections

Safety points
None

General notes
This Activity is very important since it highlights the necessity of using the correct value fuse in a particular appliance, besides teaching the pupils the correct way to wire a plug.

Apparatus list
Mains fused plugs
Electrician's screwdrivers
Wire strippers
3 core cable
Collection of different value fuses

Details for any construction
None

Activity 8:
Overloading

Objective
Appreciation that there is a limit to the load that can safely be put on any electric circuit

Experience
Overloading a fused low voltage circuit by increasing the number of lamps in the circuit

Skills involved
1. Carefully following written instructions
2. Securing the fuse wire in the circuit
3. Reading an ammeter
4. Observing and recording

Unfamiliar words
Overload

Safety points
The fuse wire will become red hot and finally melt. Pupils must be aware of this and warned to keep their fingers away from the wire.

General notes
It is important that when the pupil begins to use this apparatus only *one* bulb is placed in the sockets.

Apparatus list
Circuit overload board
4 connecting wires with 4 mm plugs
12 V supply (Low voltage unit)
Fuse wire (5 A)
Ammeter (0 – 10 A)

Details for any construction
See diagram in pupils' book, page 22, for construction of the circuit overload board. The exact dimensions are not important but a suggested size for the board is 37 cm by 12 cm. The fuse wire is supported by 2 nuts and bolts (2BA size) and the sockets where the ammeter and 12 V supply join the board are all 4 mm. The board may be raised by a strip of wood about 1.5 cm deep attached to each end underneath.

Activity 9:
Dangers of electricity

Objective
Awareness that the human body can act as a conductor of electricity

Experiences
Using simple apparatus to show (a) that the body can act as a conductor of electricity and (b) how its efficiency is increased if the hands are wet

Skills involved
1. Wiring up the circuit
2. Reading the microammeter
3. Interpreting the results

Unfamiliar words
Microammeter, dangerous

Safety points
None

General notes
It is important to keep the metal grips clean and dry.

Apparatus list
Microammeter (centre reading)
4½ V battery
3 leads with crocodile clips
Board with metal grips

Details for any construction
See diagram in pupils' book, page 24, for construction of the board with metal grips. The exact dimensions are not important but a suggested size for the board is 30 cm by 17 cm, and 1.5 cm thick. The metal grips should be about 24 cm apart and raised up on pieces of wood each about 1.5 cm thick, placed as shown in the pupils' book.

Apparatus list
(Requirements are for the teacher only)
Earthing board with model man
5 A fuse wire or 36 S.W.G. bare copper wire
12 V a.c. supply
2 leads (from board to supply unit)
1 blue lead
1 brown lead
1 green/yellow lead
1 small lead for 'shorting' (or screwdriver)

} 4 mm plugs at the ends of all wires

Optional: Model 3 pin fused plug to fit 4 mm socket

Details for any construction
See diagram 6, page 21, for construction of the earthing board with model man and the optional model 3 pin fused plug.

Activity 10:
The three pin plug — earthing demonstration

Objective
Appreciation of the need to earth electrical appliances

Experience
Possible dangers that can occur if short circuits take place when using an electrical appliance

Skills involved
1. Understanding the circuit board
2. Observing and recording
3. Interpreting results

Unfamiliar words
Blow (with reference to fuse)

Safety points
This Activity must be carried out by the teacher. Since the element will become red hot, it is important to warn pupils to keep their fingers away from that area.

General notes
Since this demonstration is in three parts, it is important that pupils attempt the questions in the correct sequence.

Activity 11:
House circuits — the ring main

Objective
Understanding the meaning of ring main circuits

Experience
Using simple models of ring main circuits to illustrate the ring main principle

Skills involved
1. Using the models according to instructions
2. Plugging in, correctly, mains appliances
3. Checking correct value of fuse for circuit

Unfamiliar words
Ring circuit, socket outlets, insulated prongs

Safety points
1. Make sure that all wires under the circuit board are secure.
2. Do not allow pupils to put the mains plug into any socket until you are satisfied that they understand fully what to do.
3. **If pupils are observing the underside of the circuit board, it must be isolated from the mains.**

General notes

Discussion is needed before pupils attempt questions.

Apparatus list

Ring main circuit board
Model ring circuit
3.5 V lamp in holder for model ring
A few household electrical appliances (e.g. hairdryer, fan heater, table lamp)

Details for any construction

See diagram 5, page 20, for construction of the ring main circuit board, and see diagram 4, page 19, for the model ring circuit.

Answers to questions in pupils' book

A letter D indicates that the answer cannot be predicted, usually because it is dependent on the results of the class experiments.

Activity 1

Questions: page 5

1. The numbers are all about the same.
2. The appliance can be used on a voltage between 230 and 250 V.
3. The numbers are higher for appliances producing a lot of power.

Questions: page 6

1. Lamp bulbs, record players, televisions, radios
2. Cookers, fires, kettles

Questions: page 7

1. (a) Low wattage
   (b) Medium wattage
   (c) High wattage
   (d) D

Activity 2

1, 2. D

3. The higher the wattage the faster the disc turns.

Activity 3

1. Slowly
2. High
3. Doubled

Activity 4

1. 1160 units

Results

Appliance	Time used per week	Power	Units	Cost
Water heater	Heating time for bath — one hour	3 kW	3	9p
Vacuum cleaner	Two hours	400 W	0.8	2.4p
Electric fire (one bar)	Thirty hours	1 kW	30	90p
Light in hall	Twenty hours	60 W	1.2	3.6p

1. Electric fire
2. D

Activity 5

1. Two coils in parallel
2. Two coils in parallel

Activity 6

1. (a) Copper
   (b) It is a good conductor
2. (a) P.V.C (plastic)
   (b) It is a good insulator
3. Rubber, porcelain, varnish cotton

Activity 7

Table lamp	3 amp fuse
Electric iron	5 amp fuse
Three bar electric fire	13 amp fuse
Television set colour	5 amp fuse
b.w.	3 amp fuse
Electric drill	5 amp fuse
Washing machine	13 amp fuse
Record player	3 amp fuse
Electric kettle	13 amp fuse
Hair dryer	3 amp fuse

Activity 8

1. D
2. It would overload the circuit and 'blow' the fuse on the power supply.
3. There are too many appliances plugged into one socket.
4. If you are running more than one appliance from a socket it is possible to overload the circuit.

Activity 9

1. Yes
2. When the skin is wet
3. Because of the water in the bathroom, wet skin and perspiration
4. It works on a long string.

Activity 10

Questions: page 26

1. Element (or wire) in 'kettle' will become red (or glow)
2. No
3. It passes through the element wire only.
4. No

Questions: page 27

1. Yes
2. It has passed through the model's body.
3. No
4. Yes

Questions: page 28

1. No
2. Yes
3. No
4. Electric drill, electric shaver, some vacuum cleaners
5. They are double insulated

Activity 11

Questions: page 29

1. Yes
2. Yes

Questions: page 30

1. Yes
2. 30 amps

3. (a) It uses less wire and cost of materials is less.
   (b) It is easier to put in extra new sockets and light switches.

Activity 12

BEDROOM

1. Fire is connected to light socket
   Circuit will be overloaded
2. Clothes are too near fire
   They could fall on to it and catch fire
3. Radio wires are pushed straight into socket without a plug
   You could electrocute yourself pushing the wire in

BATHROOM

1. Should not use electrical appliances in bathroom
   You could get an electric shock if you touched them with wet hands

2. Two appliances are sharing one plug.
   This needs a larger rated fuse. If only one appliance is in use the fuse could then be too high.

LIVING ROOM

1. Too many appliances in one socket
   Answer as 'Bathroom', question 2
2. They are also sharing the same plug
   Answer as 'Bathroom', question 2
3. Flex goes under carpet
   Cable could overheat
4. Too much insulation removed from wires coming out of plug
   You could get an electric shock if you touched the uninsulated wires

DIAGRAM 1. The ring main circuit, as used in domestic wiring.

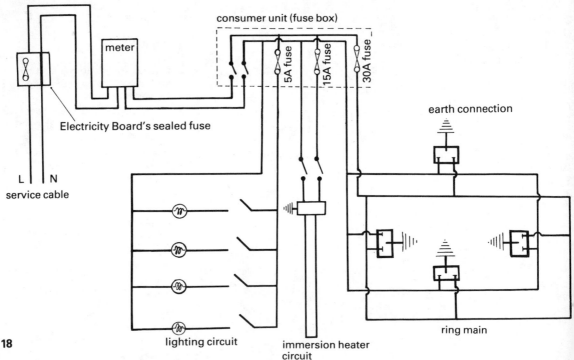

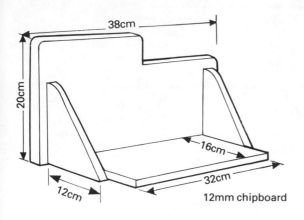

DIAGRAM 2. Construction of mount for the domestic electricity meter (Activities 2 and 3).

38cm

20cm

16cm

32cm

12cm

12mm chipboard

DIAGRAM 3. Construction of model electric fire (Activity 5).

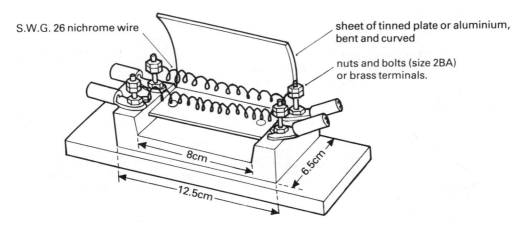

S.W.G. 26 nichrome wire

sheet of tinned plate or aluminium, bent and curved

nuts and bolts (size 2BA) or brass terminals.

8cm

6.5cm

12.5cm

DIAGRAM 4. Construction of model ring main with test lamp (Activity 11).

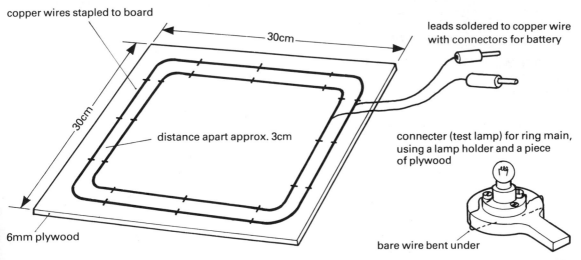

copper wires stapled to board

leads soldered to copper wire with connectors for battery

30cm

30cm

distance apart approx. 3cm

connecter (test lamp) for ring main, using a lamp holder and a piece of plywood

6mm plywood

bare wire bent under

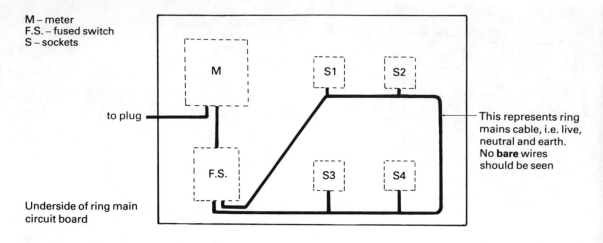

M – meter
F.S. – fused switch
S – sockets

M

S1   S2

to plug

This represents ring mains cable, i.e. live, neutral and earth. No **bare** wires should be seen

F.S.

S3   S4

Underside of ring main circuit board

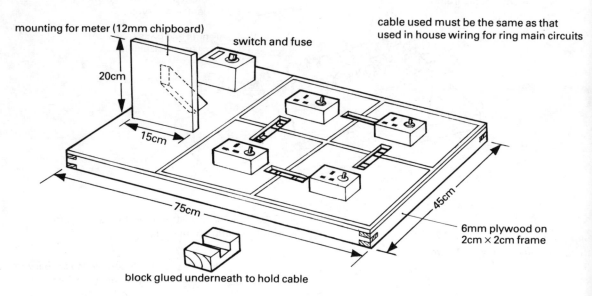

mounting for meter (12mm chipboard)

cable used must be the same as that used in house wiring for ring main circuits

switch and fuse

20cm

15cm

75cm

45cm

6mm plywood on 2cm × 2cm frame

block glued underneath to hold cable

DIAGRAM 5. Construction of ring main circuit board (Activity 11).

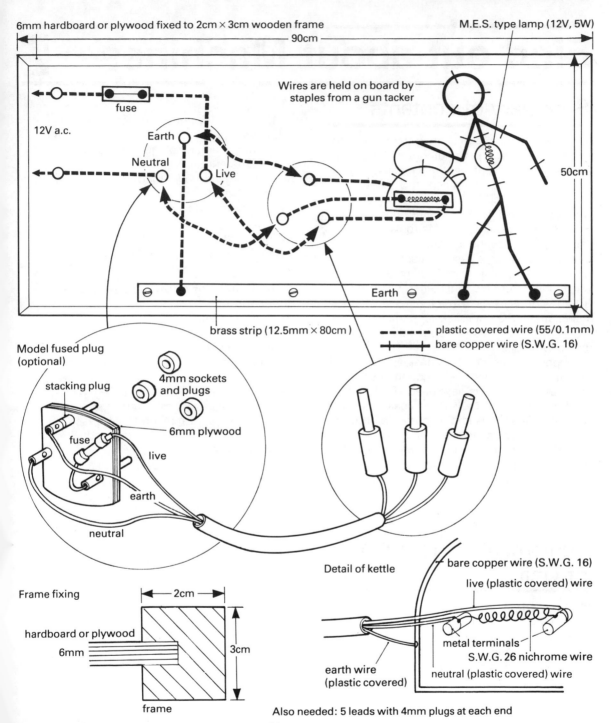

DIAGRAM 6. Construction of earthing board with model man, and optional model fused plug (Activity 10).

Find out about Machines

Summary of contents

The Unit begins by presenting the pupil with a problem — looking at photographs and then deciding if they represent machines or not. The Activities which immediately follow attempt to establish the idea that machines are not necessarily complicated, but can be fairly simple devices, such as tools (screwdrivers, spanners, drills), household items (egg whisk, scissors, secateurs) and simple pulleys. This leads to simple calculations on how much energy is used in lifting various loads. From the results of these calculations the pupils' skills, particularly observation, are tested. Do machines really make work easier?

Types of gear are next considered and from this their application and function in simple household objects is developed. The final section deals with hydraulics, again starting with simple models and then developing the principle of hydraulic systems to explain how the brakes of a car work and how to check that they are working efficiently.

Equipment list for whole of Unit

To be made

If no hook or suitable beam is available in ceiling for pulley or hoist then some kind of stand will be needed (Activities 5, 10, 11)
Meccano models to show how the following gears work (Activity 13):
   (1) worm drive
   (2) helical gear
   (3) bevel gear
Meccano trolleys fitted with clockwork motor (Activity 14):

   (1) with pulley and large gear wheel
   (2) with pulley and large gear wheel and pulley and small gear wheel on different shaft
Reduction gear model made from meccano parts (Activity 15)
Electric motor fitted on wooden base (Activity 15)
Syringes mounted on board (Activity 17)
Hydraulic press model (Activity 18)
Model car braking system (Activity 19)

To be bought or obtained from other departments

Large nails (10 cm or 15 cm)
Two metal tubes (about 24 cm long; nails must fit inside)
Haltrac hoist
Metal bending machine
Metal strips (different metals)
Several screwdrivers of different sizes
Meccano parts for making trolleys (see 'Details for any construction' under individual Activities)
Small electric motor (orbit motors are satisfactory)
Meccano parts to make reduction gears
Plastic syringes (various sizes)
Plasticine

To be collected

House bricks
Secateurs
Lawn shears
Tin snips
A car jack
Different thicknesses of wood
Screws
Blocks of wood with small holes drilled in them
Egg whisk
Adjustable spanner

Assumed normally available in laboratory

Safety goggles

Scissors
G-cramps (sometimes called G-clamps)
Half-metre rule
Forcemeter
Single pulley
Masses
Hand drill

Pieces of card
Low voltage units
Thread
4 mm plug leads
Lead foil
Suitable loads for lifting (can be made from a cardboard box containing books)

Forward planner

Activity number	Advanced planning needed	Approximate Activity time (40 min period)	Are results of a previous Activity necessary?
1	None	1 period	No
2	None		No
3	None	10 min each. Best done as a circus of experiments over 2-4 periods with discussion at the end of each about what a machine is	No
4	None		No
5	Prepare load to be lifted		No
6	None		No
7	Cut metal strips		No
8	Drill holes in a block of wood		No
9	Prepare suitable load, i.e. box of books — heavy enough to be realistic but not dangerous	4 periods. Best done in chronological order — perhaps as a demonstration with pupil participation. Could be done as a circus but the same load should be used for each Activity	No
10	Ensure a suitable support is available for pulley system		Activity 9 desirable
11			Activities 9 and 10 desirable
12	None	1 period	Activities 9, 10 and 11
13	Construct meccano models	4-6 periods. Best done as a circus over 2-3 double periods	No
14			No
15	Adjust load to get desired effect — suggest sand in a paper bag. Construct meccano reduction gear model		No
16	None	1 period	No
17	Mount syringes on board	Double period	No
18	Make model hydraulic press	Double period	No
19	Make model car braking system	Double period	No
20	None	1 period	Activity 19
Do you know?	None	1 period	Whole of Unit

Best done as a circus over 6-8 periods

Notes for teacher

Activities 1-11

The first eleven Activities are intended to establish the idea that machines need not be complicated, but can be fairly simple devices, such as levers, wheels and pulleys.

In arranging the work to be done it may be best, in terms of organisation, to cover these eleven Activities as a circus of experiments. but with larger groups it may also be necessary to provide two sets of each of the apparatus.

The loads to be lifted must not be too heavy, but at the same time, they should be realistic. If they are excessive there is a danger that a spirit of competition will lead to pupils over-exerting themselves.

When considering the types of screwdrivers for use in Activity 8, if possible, select those which have the same length blades but different handle sizes and different length blades with the same size handles.

When the pupils have completed the circus of experiments, some of the following points could be discussed:

1. The development of the machine (see 'The development of machines', pages 25-27)
2. The meaning of the word 'machine' in the light of what they have done
3. Some of the early machines used by man
4. Tools as extensions of man's limbs
5. What is the disadvantage of man's own muscle power for driving machines?
6. What is meant by the term 'industrial revolution'?

Before continuing to the next part of the Unit (gears) it may be useful to read to the class the passage on the development of machines or to use the information as a script for producing an audiotape.

Activities 13-15 (gears)

These Activities could be organised as a circus of experiments or as class experiments if sufficient resources are available. It may be an advantage to start these Activities with a discussion asking such questions as:

1. Where are gears found?

2. What is the advantage of having a bicycle with gears?
3. Why does a car need gears?

After the completion of the Activities the groups' results should be discussed and at the same time the teacher could quickly demonstrate each of the Activities again.

The following points are worth noting:
1. When the trolley just starts, the rubber band stretches more than when the trolley is moving — the force needed to start the trolley moving is greater than the force needed to keep it moving.
2. When the driving band is connected directly to the wheel shaft the trolley does not move or only moves with a very small load.
3. With the gearing engaged, the trolley moves easily and with a greater load. (The trolley moves best on a sheet of card placed on the bench.)
4. The small gear wheel would normally be connected to the engine, and the large gear wheel to the driving wheels of the car.
5. Without the reduction gear the motor, when connected to the 4 V supply, should lift a 50 g mass, but not a 100 g mass. With the reduction gear the motor should lift both loads, but much more slowly.
6. The small force supplied by the motor is converted to a large force by using the reduction gearing.

Further points about the different gears (Activity 13) are:
1. The handle is easiest to turn with worm gears, and most difficult with helical gears.
2. The worm gear output shaft turns slowest and the bevel gear output shaft the fastest.
3. In the case of the worm gear the output shaft cannot be turned at all. This is important since worm gears are used to prevent slipping, e.g. window winders, adjustable spanners.

Activity 16

This Activity introduces the section on hydraulics. It may be useful to start the section with a very brief introductory

discussion about where hydraulic systems can be found, e.g.
Car braking systems
Hydraulic jacks (some garages)
Hydraulic platforms (cleaning and replacing lamps in very high street lighting)
Hydraulic systems in mechanical shovels
Hydraulic presses in industry for shaping metals and plastics from flat sheets

Activity 17
There is much that can be demonstrated with this piece of apparatus. The main idea, however, is how we can magnify a force. Since

pressure = force per unit area
then   force = pressure × area over which the force is acting

If the areas of cross-section of the syringe barrels were 1 cm² and 10 cm² respectively and the force exerted on the small syringe was 5 N, the pressure would be 5 N/cm². This pressure is transmitted through the whole liquid and finally on to the piston of the large syringe. Therefore, the force exerted at the large syringe would be 5 × 10 = 50 N. That is, a small force exerted on the small syringe will produce a large force at the larger syringe; but the load will not move as far as the effort. Teachers could pose the questions 'Does using a machine allow us to do less work?' to which the answer is no, and 'Does it allow us to use less effort?' to which the answer is yes; i.e. machines make the work easier.

In all the experiments it may be wise to emphasise the importance of not pulling the syringe plungers out too far since this may cause them to come out altogether. If this happens air will enter and the apparatus will not work efficiently.

If there should be accidents and the system needs refilling, the following usually works.
1. Remove syringes and tubing from apparatus.
2. Remove both plungers.
3. Immerse both barrels and connecting tubing under water with the open ends of the barrels upwards.
4. By careful manipulation and tapping, all the air can be removed.

5. Push the *large* plunger in completely and then the small plunger. This helps to ensure that the plungers do not come out when the pupils are using the apparatus.

Activity 19
The car braking system works as follows: When the foot pedal is depressed the piston in the master cylinder compresses the hydraulic fluid. This pressure is transmitted through the fluid to the slave cylinders, which cause the brake shoes to come into contact with the brake drums, thus slowing the car down.

Bleeding the brakes requires two people, one to actually bleed the brakes and the other to sit in the car pumping the foot pedal when required.

A length of plastic or rubber tubing is connected to the bleeder nipple which is on the back plate of the brake drum. The free end of the tubing is placed in a jar and immersed in hydraulic fluid. *It must remain there throughout the operation* for if the air is drawn back into the system the whole process has to be repeated. The nipple is opened using a spanner.

When the brake pedal is depressed fluid is forced out of the nipple. The brake pedal is repeatedly pumped until the brake fluid entering the jar is completely free of air bubbles.

Before the operation begins and throughout the operation, the brake fluid reservoir in the engine compartment should be topped up or air will enter the system from the other end.

Finally the nipple should be properly retightened or fluid will escape and the brakes will eventually fail because of air in the system.

Historical profile: the development of machines
Manpower   Stone age man had tools made of antlers, bones, flints and stones. Even crude axes made of ivory have been discovered. With tools man can do work which would be impossible with his bare hands.

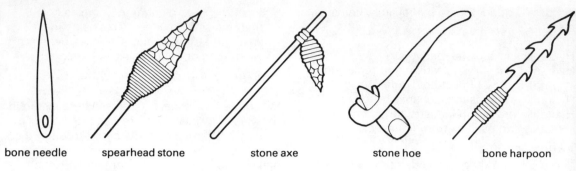

bone needle   spearhead stone   stone axe   stone hoe   bone harpoon

Some of man's earliest tools.

For centuries man had to rely on his own muscles and those of animals to do his work. Later he made simple machines such as the wheel and the pulley to make his work easier.

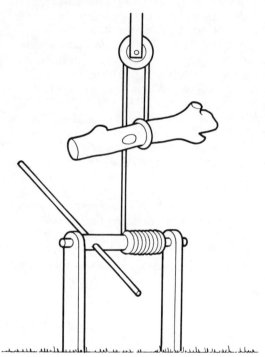

A 14th century windlass — a simple machine using a pulley.

Manpower especially in teams could produce great results, e.g. the Pyramids in Egypt, Roman roads and Stonehenge in Great Britain.

Animal power   The horse and the ox were stronger than man and could be used to drive simple machines. On this page is a drawing of a horse-powered millstone for grinding corn. Similar machines were also used for lifting water from wells and in later years even to drive machinery.

A horse driven millstone.

Water power   Water wheels were in use as early as 85 B.C. They became common in England about one thousand years ago and were machines that did not depend upon the muscle power of man or animals — the first engines.

Water is still used nowadays to drive water turbines which in turn drive generators to produce electricity. Many countries rely to a large extent on hydroelectric power stations using water turbines.

Steam engines If water is heated to produce steam the steam can be used to drive a piston backwards and forwards.

James Watt (1769) showed how the backwards and forwards motion of a piston driven by steam could be used to produce rotary motion to drive engines.

Steam driven ships were seen in the nineteenth century and the first steam locomotive ran from Stockton to Darlington in 1825 — the first railway.

Internal combustion engines In the steam engine a fuel is used to heat water in a boiler and the steam is then used to drive a piston inside a cylinder. In the internal combustion engine the fuel (petrol) is burned actually inside the cylinder and so drives the piston directly.

This is a very efficient way of burning fuel to produce movement and is the principle used in the motor car engine today.

The electric motor The electric motor changes electrical energy into movement. Electric motors can be driven either by mains electricity or by batteries. Many machines in our homes and factories are now driven by electric motors.

Main objectives and ideas

Main objectives
1. Appreciation that a machine need not be a complicated device
2. Knowledge that a machine makes a job easier to do but does not necessarily mean we use less energy (do less work)
3. Awareness that there are many types of gears and that the function of each type depends upon the job it has to do
4. Appreciation of the wide use of hydraulics in everyday life
5. Understanding the principle of operation of the car braking system

Key ideas
1. That machines can be simple as well as complicated
2. Idea of a force

3. The meaning of 'energy' and how to measure it
4. That a machine makes a job easier to do, but the energy used is the same
5. A force can be transmitted through a fluid
6. Incompressibility of fluids

Information for each Activity

Activity 1:
Looking at machines

Objective
Awareness that there are various forms of machines

Experience
Recognising a machine from a set of photographs

Skills involved
1. Ability to recognise a machine
2. Ability to observe and record according to a set of instructions

Unfamiliar words
None

Safety points
None

General notes
Discussion after the table is completed is important.

Apparatus list
None

Details for any construction
None

Activity 2:
Bending a nail

Objective
Using simple devices to increase the efficiency of the body as a simple machine

Experience
Bending a large nail with the help of two lengths of tubing

Skills involved
1. Knowing how to put the nails in the tubes prior to bending
2. Placing the nail on the brick before bending it

Unfamiliar words
None

Safety points
1. Goggles must be worn.
2. Nails must be inserted a reasonable distance inside the tubes before bending to avoid the danger of their jumping out in the process of bending.

General notes
1. Several of the pupils should be given the opportunity to try to bend the nail without any assistance before using the tubes.
2. Some discussion will be needed here.

Apparatus list
Large nail (10 or 15 cm
2 metal tubes (as used for electrical work — about 24-30 cm long)
House brick
Safety goggles

Details for any construction
None

Activity 3:
Tools used for cutting

Objective
Knowledge that the shape of tools is important when considering their function

Experience
Looking at cutting tools and comparing their structure with their function

Skills involved
1. A knowledge of cutting tools and what they are used for
2. Using the cutting tools correctly

Unfamiliar words
Secateurs, shears

Safety points
Care must be taken when using cutting tools — by their nature they have sharp edges.

General notes
The idea of a cutting tool as a form of lever should be discussed.

Apparatus list
Secateurs
Scissors
Lawn shears
Tin snips
Ruler

Details for any construction
None

Activity 4:
Using a car jack

Objective
Awareness of the function of simple machines

Experience
Using a car jack to raise a table

Skills involved
1. Correct placing of jack under objects to be lifted
2. Operating the jack

Unfamiliar words
None

Safety points
1. Make sure that the car jack is positioned correctly (reasons for this should be discussed).
2. Ensure that pupils stand well clear of the table.

General notes
The answer to question 4 should be thoroughly discussed — the safety factor is often overlooked.

Apparatus list
A car jack

Details for any construction
None

Activity 5:
Using a Haltrac hoist

Objective
Knowledge of how simple machines work

Experience
Using a Haltrac hoist to lift various objects

Skills involved
1. Supporting the hoist
2. Using the host

Unfamiliar words
Hoist, ratchet

Safety points
1. Make sure that the hoist is fixed correctly to the beam or other *safe* device.
2. Never allow pupils to put their feet directly under the load being lifted.

General notes
1. Discuss the importance of the ratchet.
2. This is also a motoring aid — discuss what it could be used for.

Apparatus list
Haltrac hoist
A suitable beam or hook or a pupose-built support
Suitable objects for lifting (box filled with books)

Details for any construction
See diagram 7, page 38 for construction of a suggested framework for the pulley support.

Activity 6:
An experiment with a G-cramp

Objective
Modifying simple machines to increase their efficiency

Experience
Using a G-cramp as a simple machine and increasing its efficiency by using an extension tube

Skills involved
1. Interpreting the meaning of the illustrations
2. Correct placing of the jaws of the G-cramp
3. Observing and recording results

Unfamiliar words
Extension, tighten, pressure

Safety points
Make sure that the extension tube fits the handle of the G-cramp correctly.

General notes
Some attempt should be made to explain why these different methods produce different results.

Apparatus list
Large G-cramp
Metal tube
Two 2p coins
Ruler
Softwood board (a small length of 25 mm × 50mm)

Details for any construction
None

Activity 7:
Using a metal bending machine

Objective
Comparison of 'man power' with 'machine power'

Experience
Using a bending machine to break a metal strip

Skills involved
1. Ability to use the machine
2. Observing and recording results

Unfamiliar words
Tighten, improve

Safety points
Care must be taken when bending metal strips with the hands — sharp edges may cut the fingers.

General notes

1. Answers to questions 1-5 should help the pupils to understand what is meant when we say that the machine makes the work 'easier'.
2. The number of bends should be the same.

Apparatus list

A metal bending machine (obtainable through normal scientific apparatus suppliers)
Some metal strips (different metals could be used, but dimensions should be the same)

Details for any construction
None

Activity 8:
Using different screwdrivers

Objective

Awareness that the structure of screwdrivers (length, size of handle) is important when considering their efficiency as a simple machine

Experience

'Driving' screws into a piece of wood using different screwdrivers

Skills involved

Using a screwdriver correctly

Unfamiliar words

Unsuitable, particular, situation

Safety points

1. It is important that small holes are previously drilled into the wood where the screws are to be driven in.
2. Screwdrivers can damage the fingers holding the screw if they slip as a result of excess pressure at the beginning of the operation.

General notes

The reason for the 'unsuitability' may not be apparent. Results should be discussed (questions 2 and 3).

Apparatus list

Large block of wood with holes drilled in it
Several screwdrivers (different lengths and different size handles)
Box of screws (all the same size)

Details for any construction
Drill holes of a suitable size in the wood.

Activity 9:
Lifting a load

Objective

Knowledge of the units of force and energy

Experience

To find the amount of energy used to lift a block

Skills involved

1. Reading a forcemeter
2. Finding lengths in metres and parts of a metre
3. Calculating the amount of energy used from a simple formula

Unfamiliar words

Forcemeter, energy, newton (unit of force), joule (unit of energy)

Safety points

1. Care must be taken when lifting the load.
2. Feet must be kept well out of the way of the load when lifting.

General notes

It is important to discuss the information given in the grey area at the top of page 12 (pupils' book).

Apparatus list

Forcemeters (25 N, 50 N)
Half-metre rule
Suitable loads

Details for any construction
None

Activity 10:
Lifting a load with a pulley

Objective
To investigate the effectiveness of the pulley as a simple machine

Experience
Using a pulley to lift a load and to measure the energy used

Skills involved
1. Reading a forcemeter
2. Measuring distances

Unfamiliar words
Pulley

Safety points
Feet must be kept clear of the raised load.

General notes
Some pupils may need some help with the mathematics involved.

Apparatus list
Single pulley
A frame or similar device for holding the pulley (some laboratories have a beam or hook facility)
Half-metre rule
Forcemeter to match suitable load
Load

Details for any construction
See diagram 7, page 38 for construction of a suggested framework for the pulley support.

Activity 11:
Lifting a load with a Haltrac hoist

Objective
Knowledge that multiple pulley systems can be used for lifting heavy loads

Experience
Using a multiple pulley system (Haltrac hoist) to lift a load

Skills involved
1. Checking that hoist is fixed correctly
2. Method of using hoist
3. Simple mathematical calculations

Unfamiliar words
Hoist

Safety points
1. Feet must be kept well out of the way of the load.
2. Make sure ratchet is working.
3. Load must not be lifted too high.

General notes
Some discussion is necessary here in comparing the results of different groups. For those pupils who are able to cope with the science it is worthwhile discussing the reasons why the hoist makes it 'easier' to lift a load.

Apparatus list
Haltrac hoist
A support for lifting the hoist if no beam is available
Half-metre rule
Forcemeters (25 N, 50 N)
Suitable loads

Details for any construction
See diagram 7, page 38 for construction of a suggested framework for the pulley support.

Activity 12:
Is it easier?

Objective
To collect information and to make decisions about the results of that information

Experience
Comparing the results of doing the same kind of work in different ways

Skills involved
Ability to check and record previous work for the purpose of making a summary and a comparison

Unfamiliar words
None

Safety points
None

General notes
Some pupils may need help on procedure — finding the necessary information and the choice of words from the word list.

Apparatus list
None

Details for any construction
None

Activity 13:
Different types of gears

Objective
Awareness of the function of different types of gears

Experience
Using tools which depend upon gears to do the jobs for which they are intended

Skills involved
1. Observing the movement of gears in different tools
2. Recording observations
3. Making decisions from observable facts

Unfamiliar words
Worm drive, bevel gear, whisk, adjustable spanner, helical gear, input shaft, output shaft, connected

Safety points
None

General notes
It is important to make simple models from such constructional kits as meccano to show how the gears fit together. Pupils can handle and observe the movements at first hand and then make comparisons with tools or other household objects.

Apparatus list
Worm drive model
Bevel gear model
Helical gear model
Egg whisk
Adjustable spanner

Hand drill complete with small twist drill

Details for any construction
See the table on page 35 for a list of the meccano parts needed to construct the gears and their stands.

Activity 14:
Why does a car need gears?

Objective
A knowledge of the application of gear systems

Experience
Using gears in a model car powered by the energy from a wound up spring

Skills involved
1. Careful observation and recording
2. Following instructions and handling apparatus carefully

Unfamiliar words
Driving band, trolley, gear wheel, engine

Safety points
None

General notes
Springs are easily damaged by over winding. Make sure that the pupils understand this important fact.

Apparatus list
Meccano trolley fitted with clockwork motor with pulley and gear wheel on driving shaft
Shaft fitted with pulley wheel, small gear wheel and two collars
Driving band
Masses to load onto trolley
Some pieces of card

Details for any construction
See the table on page 35 for a list of parts for the meccano trolley with clockwork motor. See the diagrams in the pupils' book for the construction.

Activity 15:
A reduction gear used with a small electric motor

Objective
Knowledge that gears can be used to perform many different functions

Experience
Using an electric motor together with a set of reduction gears to lift a load

Skills involved
1. Method of connecting reduction gear to motor
2. Using a low voltage unit and connecting this to the motor
3. Observing and recording

Unfamiliar words
Reduction gear, driving belt, power supply

Safety points
None

General notes
1. It will be necessary to use two clamps to secure the reduction gear apparatus and the lifting apparatus to the bench.
2. See also 'Notes for teacher'.

Apparatus list
Small electric motor fitted with pulley mounted on board
Reduction gear apparatus
Large driving belt
Low voltage supply unit
Various masses for loads
Length of strong thread
2×4 mm plug leads
2 clamps to secure the 2 models on the bench

Details for any construction
See the table on page 35 for a list of parts for the reduction gear model and the electric motor. See the diagram in the pupils' book for the construction.

Activity 16:
Hydraulics

Objective
Ability to recognise hydraulic systems by observing some of the external features of the machine

Experience
Recognising hydraulic systems from photographs

Skills involved
1. Knowledge of what hydraulic systems look like
2. Observation and recording

Unfamiliar words
Hydraulics, systems

Safety points
None

General notes
In pictures F and G hydraulic systems are not obvious — some help may be needed with these. Pupils may also need help with question 3.

Apparatus list
None

Details for any construction
None

Activity 17:
How can we magnify a force?

Objective
Knowledge of the transmission of forces through a fluid

Experience
Using specially mounted syringes connected by plastic tubing and containing water to move a heavy load

Skills involved
1. Ability to manipulate syringes
2. Ability to make careful observation and record what is seen and *felt*

Unfamiliar words
Connecting tube, syringe, tracks

Safety points
Make sure that loads are securely placed on wooden slides to prevent them falling on pupils' feet.

General notes
It is important that the pupils understand exactly what to do before they attempt this Activity. Some help may be needed in reading the instructions.

Apparatus list
Syringe board model
Wooden block to move in tracks
Various forms of loads (masses, bricks, sandbags, etc.)

Details for any construction
See diagram 10, page 40,for construction of the syringe board model.

Activity 18:
A model hydraulic press

Objective
Awareness of the applications of hydraulic systems

Experience
Using a model hydraulic press

Skills involved
1. Manipulation of the plasticine
2. Observation and recording

Unfamiliar words
Die, plunger, plasticine, underneath, exert

Safety points
None

General notes
1. The meaning of force and pressure could be discussed here and also how a small force can be 'magnified'.
2. Any small, hard, embossed object may be used as the die, e.g. a coin.

Apparatus list
Model hydraulic press
Plasticine
Lead foil
Coin, etc. for die

Details for any construction
See diagram 8, page 38, for construction of the model hydraulic press.

Activities 19 and 20:
How does a car braking system work? Checking your car braking system

Objective
Awareness of application of hydraulic systems

Experience
Using a model car braking system

Skills involved
1. Recognising differences and similarities between the model and the actual braking system
2. Ability to read instructions and carry them out
3. Observation and recording

Unfamiliar words
Brakes, pivot, springs, reservoir, brake drum, braking system, circular, spongy, cylinders, brake shoe

Safety points
None

General notes
This particular Activity should lead to some interesting discussion on why efficient brakes are essential in a car and the way they work in the real car.

Apparatus list
Model of car braking system

Details for any construction
See diagram 9, page 39, for construction of the model car braking system.

Parts required for the three gear system in Activity 13

ITEM	PART NO	QUANTITY
Angle girders	96 (9 cm)	2
Angle girders	70 (32 cm)	2
Perforated strips	3 (9 cm)	3
Double bracket	11a (25 × 12 mm)	3
Perforated strips	4 (7½ cm)	2
Perforated strips	5 (6 cm)	2
Channel bearing	160 (38 × 25 × 12 mm)	1
Double arm crank	626	3
Collar with screw	59	6
Threaded pin	115a (15 mm)	2
Axle rod	15a (11½ cm)	5
Axle rod	17 (5 cm)	1
Crank	62	3
Helical gear	211b (38 mm)	1
Bevel gear	30 (2 mm)	2
Triangular plate	76 (6 cm)	2
Trunnion	126	2
Gear wheel	31 (25 × 6 mm)	1
Worm	32 (12 mm)	1

Parts required for the reduction gear in Activity 15

ITEM	PART NO	QUANTITY
Flanged plates	52 (14 × 6 cm)	1
Triangular plates	76 (6 cm)	2
Perforated strips	5 (6 cm)	4
Crank	62	2
Collar with screws	59	1
Axle rods	16 (9 cm)	1
Axle rods	15a (11½ cm)	1
Threaded pins	115a (15 mm)	1
Gear wheel	31 (25 × 6 mm)	1
Gear wheel	27b (9 cm)	1
Nuts and bolts		8

Parts required for the trolleys in Activity 14

ITEM	PART NO	QUANTITY
Flanged plate	52 (14 × 6 cm)	1
Road wheels	187 (6 cm)	4
Gear wheel	27d (41 mm)	1
Pulley	23b (12 mm)	1
Motor non-reversing clockwork		1
Driving band	186 (6 cm)	1
Nuts and bolts		10
Axle rods	15a (11½ cm)	2
Flat trunnion	126a	4
Collar with screw	59	2

These extra items will be needed to complete trolley on page 19 of pupils' book

ITEM	PART NO	QUANTITY
Axle rod	16	1
Flat trunnion	126a	2
Collar with screws	59	2
Pinions	26 (12 × 6 mm)	1
Pulley	23b (12 mm)	1
Nuts and bolts		4

35

Answers to questions in pupils' book

A letter D indicates that the answer cannot be predicted, usually because it is dependent on the results of the class experiments.

Activity 1
1. B
2. Animal *plough.* Wind *windmill.* Water *watermill (water wheel).* Electrical *electric drill, train.* Petrol/diesel *tractor, car.*
3. D
4. Solar, tidal and nuclear power
5. **(a)** Petrol/diesel, i.e. internal combustion engine
   (b) Electrical, i.e. electric motor
   Note: There is a direct link here with *Machines on the Move.)*

Activity 2
1. No.
2. Yes
3. They give you more leverage. (Moment of the force about the fulcrum is greater.)

Activity 3
1. **(a)** They have two cutting blades.
   (b) The blades are pivoted.
2. The shears. This enables you to cut a greater amount of material (grass or hedge).
3. Secateurs, tin snips (or tools for cutting tough material)
4. Scissors, shears (or tools for materials which are fairly easy to cut)
5. Tools with long handles and short blades (again because they give you more leverage)

Activity 4
1. Using the car jack
2. A limited period of time, before becoming tired
3. No. It is only designed to carry a certain load. (The metal of the screw could shear under too great a load.)
4. If the jack slips or falls over because the surface is uneven, the car could crush the person underneath.

Activity 5
1. **(a)** Lifting a car engine out of the engine compartment
   (b) Used horizontally, to pull a vehicle out of a ditch, etc. (or other sensible answers)
2. Yes. A ratchet prevents the load falling when you let go. (Pulling the rope at the correct angle disengages the ratchet and allows you to lower the load slowly.)

Activity 6
1. You can exert a greater force using a G-cramp.
2. Because an extension tube was used. The extension tube allows you to exert a greater force (leverage increased).
3. force.
4. Holding joints in place when glued; clamping wood in position
5. For undoing wheel nuts
6. The force exerted could be too great — it could damage the nuts or the threads and it would make the nuts too difficult to remove later.

Activity 7
1, 2. D
3. Usually yes
4. Yes. Greater leverage. Can bend in exactly the same place each time.
5. Could give it a larger handle.

Activity 8
1, 2. D
3. D (size of screw head is important.)

Activity 9
1. D
2. ½ (0.5) metres
3. D

Activity 10
What to do
1. D

2. ½ (0.5) metres
3. D
Questions
1. Yes
2. The same (or slightly more due to friction at pulley)
3. The same (because you lifted the load the same distance with the same force)
4. It makes the direction of pull more convenient or allows us to use body weight to assist the pull.

Activity 11
What to to
1. D
2. 3 metres (The 6 ropes on the pulley are each shortened by ½ metre.)
Questions
1. Yes
2. Less
3. Same energy (Same load is lifted the same distance as before.)
4. You use a smaller force.

Activity 12
1. D
2. distance, easier, easier, pull, distance, same

Activity 13
2. Worm drive; Bevel gear
3. Input shaft
4. Input shaft
5. It allows a drive shaft to be at right angles to the input shaft.
6. Worm drive; Input shafts
7. Worm drive. It opens or closes the jaws. It prevents the jaws from slipping.
8. Bevel gear
9. D
10. They allow the output shaft to turn at right angles to the input shaft (more convenient to use). Output shaft turns faster.

Activity 14
What to do
8. Greater than before. The gearing has made the difference (adding the small gearwheel shaft).
9. The shaft with the small gearwheel
Questions
1. The small gearwheel; The large gearwheel
2. Slower (*Note:* The reduction gear allows the small force from the engine to be turned into a large force.)

Activity 15
What to do
3. Yes
4. No
6. Yes; Slower than before
Questions
1. force (strictly speaking, turning force or torque)
2. larger, force
3. Not necessarily. Here it is more important to lift the load. The speed does not really matter.

Activity 16
2. A. Mechanical digger
Lifts arm up and down, operates angle of bucket
B. Tractor and plough
Lifts plough clear of the ground when necessary
C. Truck
Lifts up back of truck to unload
D. Bullodzer
Lifts up or lowers 'shovel' of bulldozer
E. Car transporter
Lowers top platform to allow cars to be loaded
F. Car
Cannot see the hydraulic system. It operates the brakes (and clutch)
G. Lorry
Loading platform raised

Activity 17
What to do
6. Syringe A; When syringe B is pushed in
8. D
11. D
Questions
1. large
2. It is transmitted through water (or fluid).
3. They must be different.
4. Make syringe A smaller or syringe B bigger; or put in thicker (less compressible) fluid; or improve design to prevent loss of fluid.

Activity 18
1. An impression of the die
2. The die being pushed into the plasticine
3. At the die, or at syringe B
4. It was transmitted through the water (fluid)
5. Because the syringes are different sizes and we have magnified the force applied
6. Yes
7. Any sensible answer, e.g. in a car body factory, shaping car bodies; in a scrap yard, for crushing car bodies; in a paperworks for compressing waste paper into bales; in a steel works, shaping steel

Activity 19
What to do
1. The wheel (metal strip) turns.
2. The model brakes prevent the wheel turning.
3. They are pushed (by the syringes) on to the metal strip.
Questions
1. It is transmitted through the water (fluid).

2. To remove the brake shoes from the metal strip when the force is removed
3. shaped wooden pieces = *brake shoes*
large plastic syringe = **master cylinder**
small plastic syringe = *slave cylinder in wheels*
plastic tubing = *metal brake piping*
springs = *large return springs in wheel*
circular metal strip = *brake drum*
coloured water = *brake fluid*

Activity 20
1. Air gets into the fluid.
2. Bleed the brakes.
3. To make sure there is enough fluid in the system or so that air cannot get into the system
4. Brake shoes for wear of lining; brake piping for corrosion or leaks; master cylinder and slave cylinder for leaks

Do You Know?
1. Yes. It makes it easier for us to do a job (do work).
2. Y. Because larger handles mean we can exert a bigger force.
3. C
4. **(a)** R
   (b) Q
   (c) Q
5. A, foot pedal; B, master cylinder; C, hydraulic fluid; D, slave cylinder; E, brake shoe; F, brake lining; G, spring; H, brake drum

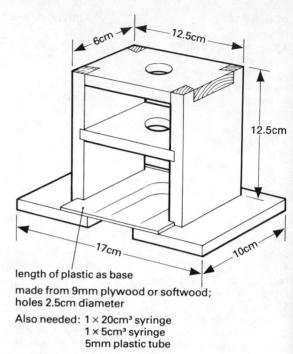

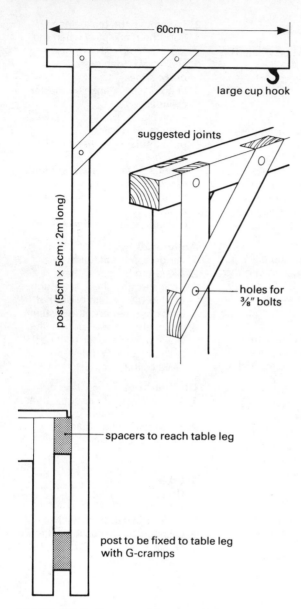

large cup hook

suggested joints

holes for ⅜" bolts

post (5cm × 5cm; 2m long)

spacers to reach table leg

post to be fixed to table leg with G-cramps

DIAGRAM 7. Suggested framework for pulley support (Activities 5, 10 and 11).

length of plastic as base

made from 9mm plywood or softwood; holes 2.5cm diameter

Also needed: 1 × 20cm³ syringe
1 × 5cm³ syringe
5mm plastic tube

DIAGRAM 8. Construction of model hydraulic press (Activity 18).

DIAGRAM 9. Construction of model car braking system (Activity 19).

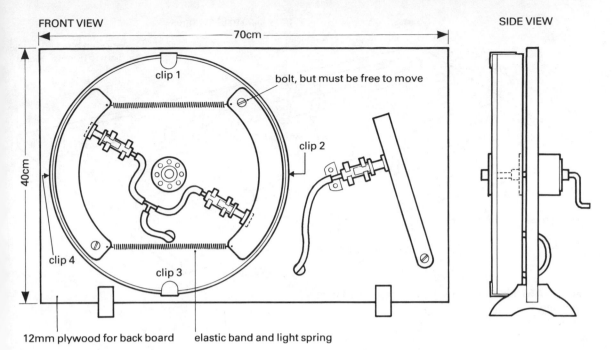

FRONT VIEW

SIDE VIEW

70cm

clip 1

bolt, but must be free to move

clip 2

40cm

clip 4

clip 3

12mm plywood for back board elastic band and light spring

Brake drum –   mild steel strip (25mm×3mm)
Perspex disc –   29cm diameter
Brake blocks –   18mm wood
Brake pedal –   12mm×35mm wood
Hydraulic gear – 1×10cm³ syringe
                 2×5cm³ syringes
                 5mm plastic tubing
                 6 terry clips
                 1 Tee piece

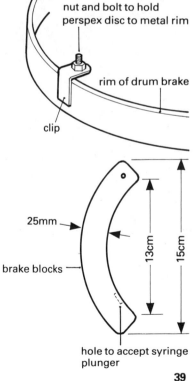

nut and bolt to hold
perspex disc to metal rim

rim of drum brake

clip

25mm

brake blocks

13cm

15cm

hole to accept syringe
plunger

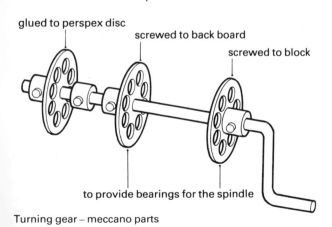

glued to perspex disc

screwed to back board

screwed to block

to provide bearings for the spindle

Turning gear – meccano parts

39

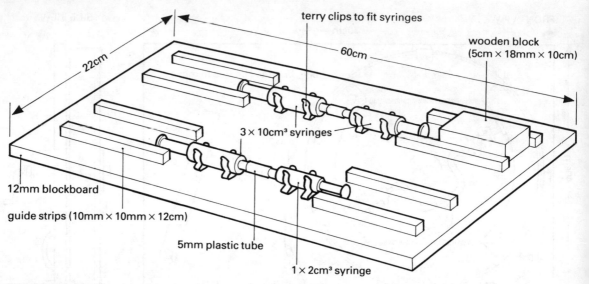

terry clips to fit syringes

60cm

wooden block
(5cm × 18mm × 10cm)

22cm

3 × 10cm³ syringes

12mm blockboard

guide strips (10mm × 10mm × 12cm)

5mm plastic tube

1 × 2cm³ syringe

DIAGRAM 10. Construction of syringe board model
(Activity 17).

Fire

Summary of contents

The Unit stresses the danger of fire in everyday life. It approaches the subject from a positive viewpoint: 'Finding out what a fuel is', 'Finding out how it burns'. The dangers are then investigated and methods of dealing with fire are illustrated. There is a quiz to test the pupils' knowledge of fire safety.

The flammability of fabrics and the effectiveness of flame resistant materials are tested. The importance of this to children's clothing is stressed. Information on types of fire extinguishers and how to use them is included.

Equipment list for whole of Unit

To be made
Delivery tubes bent at 90° with a 3cm length of rubber tubing at one end (Activity 5)
Glass jets bent at 90° (Activity 10)

To be bought or obtained from other departments
Meta fuel
Lighter fuel
Lubricating oil
0-360°C thermometer
Side arm test tubes and 1 hole bungs to fit
Baking trays
Cooking oil
Fabrics (if cannot be collected)
Washing powder
Crude oil
Proban (see Activity 15)

To be collected
Coal
Coke
Coalite
Wood shavings

Fabrics of various kinds
Bottle tops
Tin lids
Tins with lids
Paper
Sand
Potato

Assumed normally available in laboratory
Large and small heat resistant mats
Conical flasks (100ml)
1 hole bungs to fit the flasks
Methylated spirit
Boric acid
Borax
Rocksil
Ether
Paraffin
Hydrochloric acid
Sodium hydrogen carbonate
Magnesium ribbon
Candle
Sugar
Large and small beakers
Stands and clamps
Pyrex test tubes
Test tube racks
Wooden splints
Bunsen burners
Tripod
Wire gauze
Metal tongs
Spatula
0-110°C thermometers
Measuring cylinders (100cm³ and 200cm³)
Ignition tubes
Labels
Wash bottle
Safety screen
Hand lenses
Microscopes
Scissors
Stop clock

Forward planner

Activity number	Advanced planning needed	Approximate activity (40 min period)	Are results of a previous activity necessary?
1	None	2-4 periods	No
2	None	1 period	No
3	None	½ period	No
4	None (teacher demonstration)	½ period	No
5	Put thermometers into rubber bungs	2 periods	Activity 3
6	None	2 periods	Activity 5
7	None	2 periods	Activity 4
8	None	½ period	No
9	None	½ period	No
10	None	½ period	No
11	None	1½ periods	No
12	None	1½ periods	Activities 1-11
13	None	2 periods	No
14	Make squares of materials	2 periods	No
15	Squares of materials and solutions	2 periods	Activity 14
16	Squares of treated and untreated fabrics	2 periods	Activities 14 and 15

Notes for teacher

Possibly the main concern which teachers will have regarding this Unit is safety. However, if adequate attention is given to the following suggestions, teachers should feel confident in the activities being carried out safely.

1. Carefully plan class organisation.
2. Ensure all pupils wear safety goggles and aprons.
3. Keep only *small quantities* of chemicals, particularly flammable material, in the laboratory. Remember that these should be well stoppered and kept away from all sources of heat.
4. Regular checks should be made on the availability of fire-fighting equipment in the laboratory.
5. Pupils should receive instructions on what to do in case of fire.
   (a) Do not panic.
   (b) If fire is small, use heat resistant mats to smother flames.
   (c) If fire appears to be spreading, move out quickly and let your teacher deal with it.
6. Safety screens should always be used between pupils and apparatus when an activity which is being demonstrated by the teacher is considered potentially dangerous.

Most of the activities suggested in the Unit are related to either fuels or fabrics.

The first part deals with fuels and the basic idea is for the pupils to understand that fire needs fuel, heat and oxygen. The section dealing with fabrics has been designed to make pupils aware of the different kinds of fabrics used in their homes, particularly flammable material.

Teaching points

1. Under the title 'How does a fuel really burn?', the fuel itself should not burn, but only the fumes (vapour).
2. When pupils are using tin lids or bottle caps, check that the bunsen burner is removed and the lid allowed to cool before adding another substance.
3. Chip-pan fires. After the chip is placed in the oil (Activity 11) there will be a few seconds before the frothing begins. Make sure all safety precautions are taken.
4. Ways for speeding up the drying of fabrics which have been treated with fire resistant solutions (Activities 15 and 16):
   (a) fan heater
   (b) hair-dryer
   (c) radiator (winter)
   (d) thermostatically set oven or incubator
5. It is useful to make a V-shaped cut in each of the treated fabrics to distinguish them from the untreated squares (Activities 15 and 16).
6. A display of fabrics would make a worthwhile visual aid.
7. An extension to the practical work on fabrics could be to classify materials according to their origins. The preparation of a folder may be appropriate here.
8. The regulations of the Consumer Protection Act 1961 control the type of materials which can be used in the manufacture of children's nightdresses. All materials must be flame-retardant. However, there is still the point that children's nightdresses may be made by parents. Here care should be taken to ensure that the fabrics used are flame retardant.
9. It may be possible to make arrangements with the local fire brigade to demonstrate the use of fire-fighting equipment. Alternatively, various kinds of fire extinguishers could be mounted on display, including domestic extinguishers, e.g. those used in cars, for camping, etc.

Advantages and disadvantages could be discussed, i.e. that some of the fumes given off are toxic.
10. Treatment of burns. For simple burns the normal laboratory first-aid equipment should be used. If clothing is on fire, roll the person on the floor and if possible use a fire blanket. Do not remove burnt clothing or treat severe burns in any way. Call an ambulance. Remember that people suffering from burns will also be in a state of shock.

Terminology

In the writing of this Unit the use of language and the reading ability of the pupils were rated as very high priorities. Therefore it became very important to decide between correct terminology and comprehensible language, bearing in mind that the pupils might have a reading age of 10 years. In the material written for pupils the most readable and familiar word has been used wherever possible. However, for teacher information, definitions which could be accepted as scientifically correct are given here.

A gas An element or compound the molecules of which can move about freely throughout the space it occupies. Each gas has a *critical temperature below* which it becomes a vapour. *Above* this temperature it cannot be turned into a liquid by any increase in pressure.

A vapour A gas which can be turned into a liquid by increasing the pressure alone.

A fume Visible vapour consisting of small airborne particles given off by a substance. Fume has been used loosely in this Unit to cover anything given off by a fuel.

Smoke Very small solid or liquid particles colloidally suspended in the air — usually carbon.

Ignition temperature A temperature below which a substance will not spontaneously take fire; or the lowest temperature of a material at which sustained combustion can be initiated under specific conditions.

Flashpoint The flashpoint is the temperature at which the fumes (vapours) from a substance catch fire when a flame is put to them.

Flame-proof Technically 'flame-proof' cannot be applied to normal domestic textiles, but only to very specialised materials. Perhaps more correct words would be 'flame retardant', but since this would be beyond the vocabulary of this range of pupils, 'flame resistant' would be more appropriate.

(Note: In nearly all the activities pupils have been using the words 'heat resistant mat'.)

Flammable/inflammable Since both these words are used synonymously to describe the same property, flammable has been used throughout to avoid any confusion of *inflammable* meaning *not* flammable.

Domestic fuel A domestic fuel is a substance that when burnt in air gives out plenty of heat and is suitable for use in the home.

Main objectives and ideas

Main objectives
1. Awareness of what properties a good fuel should have
2. To encourage children to be aware of the dangers of fire
3. Recognition of the sources of flammable materials
4. An awareness of how to minimise the risk of fire

Key ideas
1. What a fuel is
2. Fire needs heat, fuel and oxygen
3. How a fuel's efficiency can be improved
4. Why flammable fumes are dangerous
5. Ways of putting out fire
6. Flammable and flame resistant fabrics

Resources
Films, filmstrips, slides, charts, posters and leaflets can be obtained from
Fire Prevention Information and Publications Centre
Aldermay House
Queen Street   London EC4N 1TJ

Telephone 01-248 5222.
Information can also be obtained from local Health Education Centres.

Information for each Activity

Activity 1:
Finding out what a fuel is

Objective
Awareness of the properties of a fuel

Experiences
That some fuels are better than others and that the ease and rate at which they burn are not the only factors. Availability is also important.

Skills involved
1. How to use a lighted bunsen burner when held in the hand
2. How to use a dropping pipette

Unfamiliar words
For definition of fuel see above

Safety points
1. All pupils should wear safety goggles.
2. All liquids should be kept stoppered and away from heat.
3. Only *small quantities* of flammable liquids should be kept in the laboratory.
4. Make sure that pupils remove bunsen burners from underneath bottle tops or tin lids before any substance is added.
5. Lids and bottle tops must be *dry*.

General notes
1. Any paint, cork or plastic linings on the bottle tops must be burnt off *before* the lesson.
2. Tops must *not* be made from aluminium.
3. The small amounts used in this activity (see apparatus list) can be safely allowed to burn away — there is then no need to wash the lid or bottle top.

4. If using meta fuel, take care it does not all evaporate before being lit.

Apparatus list
Bunsen burner
Tripod
Wire gauze
Heat resistant mat
Tin lids (5-8cm diameter, **not** aluminium)
Bottle tops (2-3cm diameter, **not** aluminium)
Tongs (metal)
Dropping pipette
Substances to test
Coal ⎫
Coke ⎬ *half spatula full*
Coalite ⎭
Paper (2 cm × 2 cm)
Wood (1cm cube)
Meta fuel (2mm cube, to be cut by teacher — gives off toxic vapour)
Magnesium ribbon (25mm length)
Candle wax (2mm cube)
Sawdust (not too fine — a flour-like dust can explode); *half spatula full*
Sugar *half spatula full*

Details for any construction
None needed

Activity 2:
How does a fuel really burn?

Objective
Awareness that heat is necessary to cause a fuel to burn

Experience
That no fuel burns unless there are fumes first

Skills involved
To regulate the bunsen burner in order to get the right bunsen flame. (If it is too high, draught may blow out the flame produced by the fuel.)

Unfamiliar words
For definition of fume see page 43

Safety points
1. All pupils should wear safety goggles.
2. When the smoke is coming out of the hole in the lid, the bunsen flame must be reduced.
3. Do not remove the lid until the tin has cooled down.

General notes
Ideal tin to use for this activity is a syrup tin with a 10mm hole in the lid.

Apparatus list
Tin with hole in lid
Wood or wood shavings
Paper
Bunsen burner
Tripod
Gauze square
Heat resistant mat
Metal tongs
Spatula
Splints

Details for any construction
Each of the tins used will need a 10mm diameter hole punched or drilled in the lid.

Activity 3:
Crude oil as a fuel

Objectives
To use crude oil and to become aware that it must be processed in order to be used as a 'real' fuel.

Experience
That crude oil does not make a good fuel.

Skills involved
1. To transfer only a *small quantity* of the crude oil to the lid.
2. Method of extinguishing the flame using a heat resistant mat

Unfamiliar words
Crude, processed, rocksil

Safety points
1. All pupils should wear safety goggles.
2. Important to use only a few drops of crude oil.

3. The heat resistant mat must be placed on the lid *carefully*. If the lid is upset whilst burning an accident might occur.

General notes
1. Crude oil can be obtained from the normal scientific apparatus and chemical suppliers.
2. Activity 4 should follow this activity immediately. Activity 4 is a teacher demonstration.

Apparatus list
Rocksil
Tin lid
Crude oil
Splint
2 heat resistant mats

Details for any construction
None needed

Activity 4:
(Teacher demonstration) Why are flammable fumes dangerous?

Objective
To be aware that certain fuels give off invisible vapours which can cause fire to spread very quickly.

Experience
That an invisible vapour can be a 'path' along which flame can travel from one place to another.

Skills involved
Teacher demonstration

Unfamiliar words
Important to stress the meaning of flammable (see page 00).

Safety points
1. Wear safety goggles.
2. Do not have any naked lights (bunsen burners, etc.) near the bench where this activity is being carried out.
3. Use no more than 1 cm³ of ether.

General notes
It would be appropriate to discuss with the class the dangers of smoking when using flammable liquids — including after shave, hair sprays, etc.

Apparatus list
A demonstration activity; requirements are for the teacher only.
250 cm³ beaker (pyrex)
Tripod
Heat resistant mat
1 cm³ ether (maximum)
Match or splint

Details for any construction
None needed

Activity 5:
Making crude oil into a better fuel

Objective
Understanding of how crude oil can be converted into a more efficient fuel.

Experience
That by careful heating and temperature control several substances, with different observable properties, can be produced from crude oil.

Skills involved
1. Setting up the apparatus
2. Controlled heating by using *hand-held* bunsen
3. To read accurately the 0-360° thermometer
4. Manipulation of the delivery tube and collecting tubes in each of the samples collected
5. Observation and recording must be carefully done

Safety points
1. All pupils should wear safety goggles.
2. Care when heating tube containing crude oil
3. Care when removing collecting tubes from beaker

4. Cork all collecting tubes.
5. Pupils *should not try to remove thermometers from bungs themselves.* These must be left for the technician.

General notes
1. The slower and more patiently this experiment is carried out the better the results will be.
2. The careful labelling of the tubes is important — they are needed for Activity 6.

Apparatus list
Clamp, stand and boss head
Bunsen burner
Heat resistant mat
Rocksil
Crude oil
Labels (self-adhesive)
Side arm test tube
0-360° thermometer with rubber bung
Delivery tube, bent at 90° with 3cm rubber tube
5 collecting tubes with corks
250cm³ beaker
Test tube rack

Details for any construction
1. Delivery tubes will have to be made.
2. Thermometers must be put into the bungs by the teacher or technician. (Thermometers break easily and mercury spillage is dangerous.)
3. Setting up the apparatus, if performed by pupils, will need careful organisation and instruction.

Activity 6:
Burning the liquids from different tubes (Collected in Activity 5)

Objective
Ability to assess the quality of a fuel by the way it burns

Experience
To find out by using given criteria which of the liquids produced from crude oil could be classified as a good fuel.

Skills involved
Observation and careful interpretation of results

Unfamiliar words
Smoke (see page 00)

Safety points
1. All pupils should wear safety goggles.
2. Important to use only a *few drops* of each of the fuels produced.

General notes
The liquid in tube 1 may evaporate as it is poured out, in which case the invisible fumes should be lit in the tube.

Apparatus list
5 tin lids
5 tubes from Activity 5
Rocksil
Splints
Heat resistant mat

Details for any construction
None needed

Activity 7:
Finding the 'flashpoint' of a liquid fuel

Objective
Awareness that the higher the temperature, the greater the danger of a liquid with low flash-point igniting

Experiences
1. That different fuels have different flashpoints
2. That the flashpoint of a fuel is the temperature at which fumes given off from the liquid start burning when an ignition source is applied.

Skills involved
1. Using a dropping pipette to measure a specific quantity
2. Controlled heating of water in a beaker.
3. Method of lighting fumes

Unfamiliar words
Flashpoint (see page 44)

Safety points
1. All pupils should wear safety goggles.
2. Only a small quantity of fuel should be used in each of the experiments.
3. Cold water must be used at the start of each experiment.

General notes
This should be a class activity only if the discipline and practical ability of the pupils are good. If there is doubt, the activity should be carried out as a demonstration, possibly with pupil participation.

Apparatus list
250 cm³ beaker
1 long 0-110°C thermometer
1 teat pipette
Heat resistant mat
Long splints
Liquids to test: **for pupil**
    (a) methylated spirit
    (b) lubricating oil
Liquids to test: **for teacher**
    (c) paraffin
    (d) lighter fuel
1 pyrex boiling tube
Bunsen burner
Tripod
Wire gauze

Details for any construction
None needed

Activity 8:
Taking oxygen away from fuel using sand

Objective
Awareness that heat, fuel and oxygen are needed for fire

Experience
That if oxygen is removed the fire will go out

Skills involved
Lighting and controlling a small fire and then putting it out

48

Unfamiliar words
Oxygen

Safety points
1. All pupils should wear safety goggles.
2. Make sure that the baking tray is supported on the heat resistant mats.
3. Only a small quantity of wood shavings is necessary.

General notes
It is important that pupils do not move about whilst carrying out the activity; burning wood shavings can easily be wafted off the tray.

Apparatus list
2 heat resistant mats
Wood shavings
Bunsen burner
250 cm³ beaker of sand
Baking tray

Details for any construction
None needed

Activity 9:
Using water to cool the fire

Objective
Awareness that heat, fuel and oxygen are needed for fire

Experience
That if heat is removed the fire will go out

Skills involved
Correct method of using a wash bottle to direct water onto a fire

Unfamiliar words
None

Safety points
1. All pupils should wear safety goggles.
2. Care with the use of wash bottles.

General notes
Discuss with the pupils how the water removes the heat and the fact that this prevents the fuel making the necessary fumes.

Apparatus list
2 heat resistant mats
Bunsen burner
Wood shavings
Wash bottle containing water
Baking tray

Details for any construction
None needed

Activity 10:
Keeping fuel away from oxygen using foam

Objective
To simulate the action of a foam fire extinguisher by bubbling carbon dioxide through soap solution.

Experience
That foam extinguishes a fire by settling on the surface of the burning substance and excluding oxygen, and also by reducing the surface temperature

Skills involved
1. Making up the solution to go into the flask
2. Lowering the ignition tube, containing the acid, into the solution without upsetting it
3. Putting bung with jet into the flask without disturbing the ignition tube

Unfamiliar words
Hydrochloric acid, sodium hydrogen carbonate (sodium bicarbonate)

Safety points
1. All pupils should wear safety goggles.
2. To be careful not to point the jets at other pupils in the laboratory or at themselves.
3. Have plenty of clear bench space just in case some of the burning wood is blown off the tray.
4. Stress care when using acid.

General notes
Some careful explanation will be needed on how to lower the ignition tube into the flask without upsetting the acid.

Apparatus list
2 heat resistant mats
Bunsen burner
Wood shavings
100 cm³ conical flask
Washing up liquid
Dilute hydrochloric acid
Sodium hydrogen carbonate
Spatula
Measuring cylinder (or beaker marked at 50 cm³)
Baking tray
Ignition tube
Glass jet in rubber bung (to fit conical flask)

Details for any construction
1. Make glass jets and secure them in rubber bung (to be carried out by technician).
2. Before starting the activity check that bung will fit flask.

Activity 11:
(Teacher demonstration)
Chip-pan fires

Objective
Knowledge of how to deal with fires in the frying-pan

Experience
When a wet chip is put into hot oil, the water from the chip boils making the oil froth over, which could cause a fire.

Skills involved
Careful observation: this is a teacher demonstration

Unfamiliar words
None

Safety points
1. Use a *dry* thermometer for stirring oil.
2. Turn the burner out before chip is placed in the oil.
3. Remove hands well clear of the beaker.
4. After the experiment let the apparatus cool down before removing anything.
5. Use safety screen.

General notes
The frothing over is caused by water on or in the chip boiling suddenly. This happens when either the oil is too hot or too many chips are put into the oil together.

Apparatus list
100cm³ graduated beaker
Wire gauze
Tripod
Bunsen burner
0-360° thermometer
Knife (to peel and cut potato)
Safety screen
2 heat resistant mats
Baking tray
Potato to make chips
Metal tongs
Cooking oil

Details for any construction
None needed

Activity 12:
Can you pass the fire safety test?

Objective
To revise the results and work carried out in earlier activities, first by discussion then by the written test.

Activity 13:
What do the fibres of fabrics really look like?

Objective
To recognise that fibres have different properties and structures

Experience
Fibres taken from different fabrics can be distinguished from each other when seen under a microscope.

Skills involved
1. How to use a microscope
2. Correct method of taking fibres from the fabric
3. Matching fibres with diagrams

Unfamiliar words
Fibre, fabric, synthetic, names of fabrics

Safety points
If fibreglass is used take care when handling it. Forceps could be used.

General notes
In the selection of fabrics make sure there are natural and man-made ones.

Apparatus list
Samples of six different fabrics
(the samples are best put into containers and labelled, e.g. silk, cotton, wool, rayon, nylon, polyester, fibreglass)
Hand lens
Microscope
Microscope slide
Scissors

Details for any construction
None needed

Activity 14:
Testing fabrics to see how easily they burn

Objective
Awareness that different fabrics behave differently when burnt

Experiences
1. That fabrics burn for different lengths of time with different results
2. That some fabrics remain hot or have hot drips even when flame has gone out

Skills involved
1. Correct handling of tongs when holding burning fabric
2. Accurate use of stop clock

Unfamiliar words
Scorch

Safety points

1. All pupils should wear safety goggles.
2. Great care is needed when burning fabrics.
3. Always keep the burning fabric over the tin lid or metal dish.

General notes

1. Working with a partner in this activity is essential.
2. Some organisational techniques should be explained. Work out who does what in advance.
3. Useful to discuss advantages and disadvantages of the fabrics apart from their flammability.

Apparatus list

Samples of untreated fabrics (see list of fabrics suggested for Activity 13)
Metal tongs
Bunsen burner
Metal dish (or large tin lid)
2 heat resistant mats
Stop clock
Paper

Details for any construction
None needed

Activity 15:
How safe is flame-proofing?

Objective

To show that a fabric can be made more flame resistant when treated with certain chemicals

Experience

That treated fabrics burn for a shorter lengths of time than the same untreated fabrics

Skills involved

1. Correct handling of tongs when holding burning fabric
2. Accurate use of stop clock
3. Drying the treated fabric — discuss what would be the best way to do this

Unfamiliar words (see page 00)

Flame-proofing, flame retardant, flame resistant

Safety points

All pupils should wear safety goggles when burning the treated fabrics.

General notes

1. Can be done in one lesson if a quick method of drying is available, e.g. oven, fan heater, hair-dryer, etc.
2. If slower method only is possible, e.g. over radiator, window ledge, postpone burning until next lesson.

Apparatus list

Samples of fabrics (see Activity 13)
Beaker containing flame retardant solution
Tongs (metal)
Bunsen burner
Metal dish or tin lid
Heat resistant mat
Stop clock
Scissors
Flame retardant solution is made by dissolving:
  43.5g borax and
  18.5g boric acid
  in 500cm³ water
'Proban' is a commercial preparation that could be tried also

Details for any construction
None needed

Activity 16:
Does washing affect the flame-proofing?

Objective

To show that washing with soap or detergent can affect the flame resistant properties of the fabric.

Experience

That soapy detergents (made from animal or vegetable fats and oils) have a different effect from synthetic detergents (made from petroleum products)

Skills involved
Careful organisation is necessary here.
1. Keep the soapy and synthetic detergent washed fabrics separate.
2. Best way of drying fabrics
3. Careful recording of results important

Unfamiliar words
Soapy detergent, synthetic detergent

Safety points
All pupils should wear safety goggles when burning fabrics.

General notes
Careful observation and a method of distinguishing between treated and untreated fabrics (see Teaching points, page 43) are important.

Apparatus list
2 squares of flame resistant fabric
2 squares of untreated fabric (*must be the same kind of fabric as above*)
Metal tongs
Metal dish or lid
2 beakers (400 cm³)
2 stirring rods
Soapy detergent (Lux or Dreft)
Synthetic detergent (Tide or Daz)
Measuring cylinder (200 cm³)
Stop clock
Labels
Spatula
Heat resistant mat
Scissors

Details for any construction
None needed

Answers to questions in pupils' book

A letter D indicates that the answer cannot be predicted, usually because it is dependent on the results of the class experiments.

Activity 1
1. Paraffin, wood
2. They give heat, burn for a long time and light easily.
3. Paraffin, wood
4. lights
5. gives off
6. burns
7. does not give off
8. does not leave

Activity 2
1. No
2. Heat
3. The fuel
4. Heat
5. No
6. Wood
7. Wood
8. Fumes*

Activity 3
1. Yes
2. Orange or red
3. Yes
4. Yes
5. No

Activity 4
1. Fumes
2. No
3. No
4. Yes
5. He could light the fumes and start a fire.
6. people did not see the warnings about smoking.

Activity 6
1. 1
2. 5
3. 1
4. 2
5. Yes

Activity 7
1. Meths or petrol
2. About 25°C
3. Meths, petrol
4. Low
5. Petrol
6. Alcohol, low, flashpoint

Activity 8
1. Yes
2. Fairly
3. Very
4. No
5. Too heavy; could not throw it; would need too much

Activity 9
1. Yes
2. Yes
3. Yes
4. Yes
5. Plenty of it; can be used in a hose and easily sprayed over fire

Activity 10
1. A lot of froth and foam were made.
2. Yes
3. Yes, but it leaves a mess sometimes.*

Activity 11
1. Yes
2. Frothing and spitting; oil overflows
3. The overflowing oil would burn.
4. Wet
5. 100°C
6. Yes
7. Try 1 or 2 first to see if temperature is right.
8. Cover pan with a *damp* towel.
9, 10, 11 D

Activity 12
1. Raise the alarm.
2. Call the fire brigade.
3. Closed
4. 999
5. Your name, and address of fire.
6. No
7. Someone could knock into it. A child could grab the handle.
8. Matches
9. A fire guard
10. No
11. 1. Things being placed too close to it.
    2. Worn flex
    3. Faulty plug/overloaded socket
12. Roll in a blanket.
13. With sand
14. Bed clothes can catch fire if you fall asleep.
15. The petrol fumes could catch fire.
16, 17 D
18. Sand or water
19. Test the oil with one chip.
20. Cover with a damp cloth, turn off heat, leave to cool.

Activity 13
1. No
2. Some

3.
Polyester	Very fine, fuzzy
Rayon	Wavy, thick
Wool	Wavy, rough, thick
Linen	Thick, slightly wavy
Nylon	Straight, smooth
Cotton	Straight, thick, rough

*In the 1979 printing of the pupil's books the questions in these activities were numbered incorrectly. These answers apply to the corrected numbers.

FIRE

4.
Wool	Nylon
Linen	Rayon
Cotton	Polyester
Silk	Acrylic
	Acrilan
	Terylene
	Orlon
	Dralon
	Fibreglass

Activity 14
1. Rayon, cotton, polyester, nylon
2. Wool, linen
3. Polyester, nylon
4. All of them
5. Cotton, nylon, polyester

6. Polyester (some nylon)
7. They could spread the fire.
8. Wool, or linen
9. It does not burn very well.
10. Polyester, nylon, cotton
11. They burn very quickly, and polyester would burn onto the child.

Flame-proofing fabrics
1. The girl is wearing a loose nightdress. The girl is too near the fire.
2. No
3. A fireguard
4. Polyester, cotton
5. Wool, linen
6. Roll her in a blanket.

7. Call a doctor.
8. See if it is flame-proof.
9. They do not flap about.

Activity 15
1. Yes, cotton (and others)
2. Polyester, but slower
3. Cotton, linen, rayon

Activity 16
1, 2. D.
3. No
4. Yes
5. Synthetic
6. Biological
7. Water softeners, dry cleaning, age of material
8. Soapy detergents

Grow Your Own

Summary of contents

The Unit is designed to give pupils courage, confidence and experience in growing plants, so that where facilities are available at home or in school this experience may be extended using the basic skills.

Pupils learn how to handle plants and seedlings, and discover a little about the conditions needed for seeds to germinate. They are introduced to two common houseplants and learn how to take cuttings and propagate them.

The Unit also shows how some edible seedlings (bean sprouts and mustard) can be grown very easily, and encourages pupils to think about the cost compared with buying them ready grown.

There are several Activities on soil, which introduce the different types of soil, what it consists of and what substances in it might be useful for plant growth. The subject is broadened to examine the animals present in soil samples, and the role of earthworms is emphasised.

Equipment list for whole of Unit

To be made
None

To be bought or obtained from other departments
Mung beans or alfalfa seeds
Mustard seeds
Seed selection (for Activities 4 and 6)
Domestic sieve
Cotton wool or nappy liner (1 roll)
Potting composts
Seed compost
Growing compost
Cutting compost
Sand
Polythene bags, with twist closures, large enough for seed trays (6 or 7 per group)
Nutrient solution (Fisons Growmore or Phostrogen)
Seed labels (6 per group)
Dibbers (1 per group)
Powdered chalk
B.D.H. soil test solutions for nitrogen, phosphates and potash (buy in litres and decant); also tin rods (1 per group) and colour charts (1 per group)
Seed trays (3 or 4 per group)
Plant pots (4 or 5 per group)
Guide to soil animals

To be collected
Jam jars (2 per group)
Teaspoons (1 per group)
Net to cover jam jar (1 per group)
Empty margarine or yoghurt pots (5-6 per group)
Crocks, i.e. broken plant pots or stones (for 3 pots per group)
Off cuts of Fablon
Gloss paint (ends of tins)
Newspaper
Worms
Soil samples (3 buckets of 3 kinds and ½ bucket of another 6 kinds)
Tradescantia plants
Chlorophytum plants
Library books for identification of soil animals

Assumed normally available in laboratory
Detergent
Transparent beakers
Rubber bands
Drainage trays to stand plant pots and seed trays on
Scissors
3 or 4 buckets
Small watering can
Test tubes
Corks
Filter funnels
Filter paper
Trowels

Forward planner

This Unit is best done in spring and summer. It should not be attempted during January and February.

Activities 1, 2, 3, 4, 6, 7 and 9 involve the use of seed trays and/or plant pots. It is necessary to plan where these can be kept, along with drainage trays to catch moisture.

Activity number	Advanced planning needed	Approximate Activity time (40 min period)	Are results of a previous Activity necessary?
1	None	15-20 min first day, then 5-10 min per day (4-5 days) for watering	No
2	None	15-20 min initially, then 5 min per day (3 days) watering time	No
3	None	20-30 min	No
4	Dilute nutrient solution	1 period	No
5	Collect empty yoghurt and margarine cartons	1 period	No
6	Plant trays of seeds 2-3 weeks before, in case those from Activity 4 are not ready	1 period	Could use seedlings from Activity 4 if timing allows
7	Obtain houseplants (at least 1 per group) which can be moved to a larger pot	1 period, depending on the number of plants available	No
8	Grow good sized Tradescantia plants (start at least one term in advance)	1 period	No
9	Grow sufficient Chlorophytum plants to leave one runner per group of pupils (start at least one term in advance)	20-30 min	No
10	Collect 2 or 3 soil samples	1 period, depending on the number of soil samples	No — but can be done concurrently with Activity 11
11	Ask pupils to bring some soil samples, in addition to those provided	30 min	Useful to do concurrently with Activity 10
12	Collect some fresh soil 1-2 days before the lesson, if it cannot be collected during the lesson	1 period	No
13	Collect earthworms	20 min +	No
14	Collect 3 buckets of 3 kinds of soil	20 min initially, then 30 min 2 weeks later	Use Activity 11 to name the soil and if possible use same soil in next three Actitivies
15 16 17	Collect soil samples as in Activities 11 and 14. Decant and relabel soil test solutions	15-20 min for each soil sample. Use several soils. Use 2-3 periods to test all soils	These are best done as a group. There is a link here with Activities 11 and 14

Notes for teacher

Because this Unit is largely concerned with growing plants, it is not wise to start it during January and February. It has been sucessfully done in autumn, but the best time to start is spring or summer.

It is important to decide on the purchase of seeds and compost before you start (see 'Equipment list for whole of Unit', and notes on Activity 4, below).

Make sure a responsible person keeps an eye on all the seeds and plants and waters them as necessary, in case a pupil is away ill or forgets.

Activtiy 1

For this Activity it is best to use mung beans or alfalfa seeds. These can be obtained from health foods shops or from Thompson and Morgan, Crane Hall, London Road, Ipswich, Suffolk IP2 0BA. The sprouts are ready for eating when they are 2-3 cm long (usually about 5 days; if more than 10 days the taste may be spoiled). These are delicious to eat in salads, fried with Chinese type meals or in soups. The domestic science department may be willing to cooperate here.

Activity 2

Mustard seeds are frequently used in schools, but the conditions usually make the resulting mustard unfit for eating. In the pupils' book, cotton wool is listed under 'You need'. In fact a roll of nappy liner is better. It can easily be cut to fit the dishes and the gauze stops the fluff from being carried up with the seed leaves, which makes the crop unpalatable.

When the mustard is ready, suggest that pupils cut it and use it to make sandwiches in the domestic science room, provided you are satisfied it has been grown reasonably hygienically.

Activity 3

Clay plant pots can in the long run be cheaper than plastic. Plastic pots can be used and crocks are not necessary with them.

Whole mustard plants are grown because this illustrates the point that most of our foods are part of a plant. It also enables the pupils to see, cheaply, a whole plant grow.

Activity 4

A wide variety of seeds can be grown. If you do the Activity in spring, and you have a school garden, lobelia or lettuce can be grown for planting out. The small alpine strawberry 'Baron Solemacher' is also very good as it makes an edging plant and will go on fruiting into the autumn term. It must be grown early if you are to get a crop the first year.

The best method of choosing seeds is to read the notes on the back of the packets and look for the factors listed below:

1. Short germinating time
2. Seeds that can be planted in trays for later planting out (many varieties such as raddish which should be sown outdoors are wasted in seed trays)
3. Temperature: If you do not have a greenhouse, propagator or room in which the temperature does not drop at nights or weekends, do not chose varieties that require constant warmth.

Growing

Keep the seed packets; you may need to look at the instructions again. Label the trays, as seedlings rarely look like the plant in the early stages and pupils can become very confused. Sow in rows unless directed otherwise. It is much easier to tell which are the intended plants. A general rule is to cover the seeds with their own depth of soil. It is important to keep all the trays warm and damp.

In this Activity all the seeds should germinate, but the best growth will be in those grown in compost or those watered with nutrient solution.

Even if these seedlings grow too late for Activity 6, try to let the pupils prick them out and grow them on, either at school or at home.

Activity 5

This Activity can be done at any time during the Unit.

The newspapers are to prevent damage to the benches.

Fablon or gloss paint make excellent covering materials. Do not use spray on paint (it tends to dissolve the cartons) or poster paint (this washes off). Do warn pupils to be

57

careful with the scissors, and *always* to work on the bench.

Activity 6

It is most important when pricking out seedlings to avoid damage to the stem and root hairs. Therefore seedlings should *always* be held gently by the leaves.

Seedlings should be pricked out before they become large enough to crowd or shade each other. Seed packets often give some relevant information. You can use the seedlings from Activity 4, but it is best to have some extra trays prepared for the lesson.

Activity 7

The two reasons for transplanting are:

1. The plant becomes pot bound (the roots have filled all the space available and may be seen coming through the hole in the base of the pot)
2. When you wish to move them or regroup them for aesthetic reasons

As in Activity 6, it is important not to damage the stem or roots. If plants are pot bound it is best to use a pot just one size larger than the one they are in.

Activity 8

Many plants can be propagated from cuttings, but the ease with which this can be done varies. Tradescantia is very easy to propagate in this way, and although cutting compost is suggested here because it is the correct compost to use, in general Tradescantia will grow in most soils.

The most attractive plants are obtained if several cuttings are put into one pot.

It is a good idea to use the home-made pots (from Activity 5) for this Activity. Pupils will then be able to take home attractive houseplants at the end of the Unit, without the problem of paying for plant pots.

Activity 9

The houseplant Chlorophytum (Spider plant) is very easy to grow from aerial runners so it is a good idea to have a stock of 4 or 5 in the lab or greenhouse.

Activity 10

Diagram 11, page 67, shows the results expected after 30 min.

It is a good idea to allow pupils to use at least two different soils and compare them.

The waiting period of 20 min while the soil settles can be very boring for the pupils. It is therefore a good idea to run this with Activity 11.

Activity 11

This Activity includes a simplified key. Many gardening books and seed packets refer to these soil types.

Activity 12

The names of the animals are not important, but the key from the *Life Spotting* pupils' book can be used. Pupils should realise that (a) the soil contains many animals and (b) most of the animals are useful and help to put nutrients into the soil by assisting in decay.

Activity 13

The experiment illustrates the important job done by earthworms in moving soil. Many minerals are washed from the top of soil to lower levels by rain water. The earthworms ingest the lower soil, which passes through their gut and is carried to the top and excreted when the worms come to the surface, usually at night.

It is best to keep the jam jars in a darkened cupboard and not to fill them too full.

Activity 14

Pupils should be made aware that some soils grow certain kinds of plants better than others and that many plants will grow only on certain kinds of soil.

At least three different kinds of soil should be used for this Activity. Give all the pots the same amount of water. The time taken for the crop to grow will vary considerably with the types of soil used. The crops should all be cut and harvested at the same time.

Activities 15-17

The test solutions are sold by British Drug Houses (B.D.H.) but the numbering on the bottles causes confusion. It is better for the pupils if the technicians decant the solution into dropping bottles (the plastic ones with integral droppers are ideal) and label them: Nitrogen 1,2; Phosphate 1,2; Potash 1, 2.

You can buy the colour charts to go with them from B.D.H. Order one per group and also one tin rod per group. Buying the solutions like this is cheaper than buying soil test kits; it is easier for the pupils to use this method.

If the school has a garden and you have time, there is plenty of extension work that can be done. *Be Your Own Gardening Expert* published by Pan Britannica Industries gives some good ideas and help.

Main objectives and ideas

Main objectives
1. To teach pupils enough about growing plants to enable them to do this in the future
2. To show them that the growing of plants need not necessarily be expensive or require a great deal of expensive equipment

Key ideas
1. The care and handling of seeds, seedlings, cuttings and plants
2. The make-up of soil and ways in which it can vary and that this can affect the plants

Relevant information
1. Videotape BBC and ITV gardening programmes could be obtained.
2. Local parks departments will often be happy to help with advice or demonstrations, as will Botanical Gardens.
3. Seed merchants' catalogues are often useful and quite inexpensive. (You can often buy last year's copies.)
4. Free or cheap publications are available from Pan Britannica Industries Ltd., Waltham Cross, Herts.
5. Visit local garden centres. They often have free handouts on planting and propagation.
6. Books: Pan Britannica Industries, *Be Your Own Gardening Expert* and *Be Your Own House Plant Expert; Readers Digest Encyclopaedia of Garden Plants* (possibly for the school library).

Information for each Activity

Activity 1:
Easy food

Objective
Awareness that certain foods can be grown without the use of soil or compost

Experience
Growing salad foods in a jam jar

Skills involved
1. To write simple records (name of seed used, date started, date finished)
2. To be able to manipulate simple apparatus
3. To follow stage by stage instructions
4. To 'read' diagrams

Unfamiliar words
Names of seeds used, hydroponics, shoots, polythene, sieve

Safety points
None

General notes
1. Some of the seeds used may have unfamiliar names — e.g. alfalfa — and some explanation may be needed.
2. Since about 6-8 days are required to complete the Activity, arrangements must be made for groups to carry out the necessary tasks.

Apparatus list
Jam jar
Teaspoon (plastic)
Piece of fine net
Beaker
Some packets of seeds (e.g. alfalfa)
Polythene bag, e.g. freezer bag
Sieve (or collander)

Details for any construction
None

Activity 2:
The cost of growing mustard

Objective

To appreciate that it is more economical to grow some of our own food than to buy it in shops

Experiences

1. Growing mustard seed by the hydroponic method
2. Comparing the cost of growing mustard with buying the *same* quantity in the shops

Skills involved

1. Preparing the plastic dish
2. Cutting the cotton wool to size
3. Placing the seeds on the cotton wool as instructed
4. Ability to record information correctly
5. Ability to carry out simple computation and estimation

Unfamiliar words

Cotton wool, teaspoonful, mustard, scatter, seedlings, polythene

Safety points

None

General notes

1. Again, this Activity will take several days to complete and it is therefore important that pupils monitor the growing process each day.
2. If pupils sample the mustard by itself, the 'hot' taste may be a little off-putting. It may be a worthwhile exercise to show them how to use the mustard on a salad.

Apparatus list

Cardboard or plastic dish (must be clean)
Cotton wool
Mustard seed
Drainage tray (plastic seed tray with sand in the bottom)
Plastic bag
Rubber band
Large darning needle (to make holes in plastic dishes)

Details for any construction
None

Activity 3:
Growing whole plants

Objective

Familiarity with the growth of plants at different stages of development

Experience

To grow mustard seeds to obtain mature plants

Skills involved

1. Preparation of pot
2. Preparation of compost prior to sowing the seeds
3. Sowing seeds according to instructions
4. Putting pot into plastic bag and making secure
5. Recording progress of development

Unfamiliar words

Potting compost, crocks, drainage, twist closures, germinate

Safety points

None

General notes

Since this Activity may take several weeks before the 'plant' reaches maturity, it is important that during this time pupils realise that it must be cared for, i.e. it will need watering, plenty of light and a certain amount of warmth. It may also need support as it grows.

Apparatus list

10 cm plant pot (crock or plastic)
Potting compost (loam or peat based)
Mustard seeds
Crocks or small clean stones (if plastic pots are used these are not necessary)
Drainage tray (seed tray with sheet of plastic covering the bottom with about 3 cm of sand on top of this — keep damp)
Polythene bag (freezer bag)
Twist closures (as used for freezer bags)

Details for any construction
None

Activity 4:
Growing seeds

Objective
Growing seedlings using the seed tray method

Experience
Preparing seed trays, sowing seeds and growing on to the seedling stage

Skills involved
1. Filling seed trays with sand or compost according to instructions
2. Preparing surface of sand or compost to accept seeds
3. Preparing labels for each tray
4. Placing prepared tray into polythene bag and making secure
5. Maintaining and recording progress of the development of the seeds

Unfamiliar words
Nutrient solution, furrows, instructions, germinated

Safety points
None

General notes
1. Make sure that boxes or trays are clearly labelled.
2. Since there are many stages for the pupils to complete, a step by step teaching approach may be more effective.
3. It is important to remember that adequate space will be required to 'house' the seed trays and that continued care will be necessary.

Apparatus list
3 seed trays, labelled A, B and C
Plant labels
Seeds
Sand (**not** building sand)
Seed compost
Nutrient solution (solution of Phostrogen)
Drainage tray
2 large polythene bags
2 twist closures

Details for any construction
None

Activity 5:
Make your own plant pots

Objective
Awareness that containers for growing plants from seeds can be made from disused plastic cartons

Experience
Making plant pots from used plastic containers

Skills involved
Ability to use scissors for making holes in plastic containers

Unfamiliar words
Cartons, detergent, container

Safety points
The points at the ends of scissors can be dangerous; make sure that pupils know the correct way to hold them and the correct method of holding the plastic container.

General notes
Since plant pots are not cheap, it is a good idea to use as many different kinds of plastic containers as possible in order to encourage pupils to re-cycle used material.

Apparatus list
Empty plastic containers (e.g. those used for yoghurt, margarine, washing up liquid)
Scissors
Paint or Fablon
Paint brushes (if paint is used)
Detergent
Newspaper
Felt tip pen (permanent colour)

Details for any construction
None

Activity 6:
Pricking out seedlings

Objective
An understanding of the need to transfer young plants (seedlings) in order to allow them more room to develop

Experience

Transferring (pricking out) seedlings from seed tray to plant pots

Skills involved

1. Preparing compost
2. Writing label
3. Correct way of removing seedling
4. Securing seedling in its new position in the plant pot
5. Putting pot into polythene bag
6. Recording development of plant

Unfamiliar words

Nutrient solution, separate, dibber, crowded

Safety points

None

General notes

Make sure that the compost is damp throughout. It is best to mix compost in a bowl before putting it into the pot. If you squeeze a handful of compost and it remains as a ball without water dripping out of it this is about the correct consistency, but if water drips from between your fingers, the compost is too wet.

Apparatus list

Plant pots or 'home made' plastic tubs (these should be about 5 cm diameter)
Dibber
Growing compost (loam based or peat based)
Sand (**not** builders' sand)
Labels (plastic are best)
Felt tip pen (permanent)
Tray of seedlings
Large polythene bag
Twist closure
Nutrient solution (solution of Phostrogen)

Details for any construction
None

Activity 7:
Transplanting

Objective

To appreciate that as pot plants grow the roots need more room for development and the plant should be transferred to a bigger pot

Experience

Transplanting or potting-on plants from small pots to larger pots

Skills involved

1. Mixing compost
2. Preparing pot to accept plant
3. Correct way of holding plant
4. Securing plant in its new pot
5. Caring for plant after transplanting (e.g. providing light, warmth and water)

Unfamiliar words

Squeeze, crocks, reaches

Safety points

None

General notes

When transferring the plant from one pot to another it is sometimes difficult to remove the 'root ball' from the smaller pot. In order not to damage the roots or the leaves the following procedure may be found useful.

Stretch the hand out flat, palm down. Separate first and second fingers and place them around the stem, as low down as possible. Turn the pot upside down and tap the bottom sharply. The plant should then come away easily.

Apparatus list

Potting compost (e.g. John Innes No. 2)
Bucket
Small watering can
Crocks (or small clean stones)
Plant pots (about 10 cm diameter)
Dibber or plastic teaspoon
Plants already growing in small pots
A trowel or small length of dowel rod for mixing compost

Details for any construction
None

Activity 8:
Taking cuttings

Objective

Awareness that new plants can be grown by taking cuttings (parts of stem) from mature plants

Experience
Taking cuttings from various plants

Skills involved
1. Preparing pot and compost
2. Correct method of preparing cutting
3. To transfer prepared cutting to small pot and to secure in the compost

Unfamiliar words
Cuttings, swelling

Safety points
None

General notes
1. The best compost to use for cuttings is a mixture of 2 parts sand (sharp sand is best) and 1 part peat. No nutrient solution or fertiliser should be used; these can damage the roots.
2. If possible a propagating unit should be used. If this is not available, it will help to place the pots containing the cuttings in polythene bags in a warm, sunny place.
3. Other plants that can be tried are geraniums, fuchsias, coleus, impatiens and begonias. Late spring is a good time to take cuttings, except for geranium (pelargonium) cuttings which are best taken in late summer.

Apparatus list
5 cm plant pots
Compost
Dibber
Crocks or small clean stones
Bowl or bucket to mix compost
Small watering can
Some mature plants

Details for any construction
None

Activity 9:
Growing houseplants

Objective
Knowledge that some plants produce young plantlets at the end of long trailing stems, which if put into compost will root and grow into a mature plant

Experience
Using plantlets from Chlorophytum to grow into a houseplant

Skills involved
1. Preparing pot and compost
2. Removing plantlet from parent plant
3. Securing plantlet in compost
4. Caring for plant

Unfamiliar words
Runner, Chlorophytum

Safety points
None

General notes
It might be a good idea to use the plastic bag method until plant becomes established. Strawberries are a good example of self layering outdoor plants.

Apparatus list
5 cm plant pots
Dibber
Compost
Crocks (or small clean stones)
Mature Chlorophytum with plantlets
A few strawberry plants showing runners (if possible)
Small watering can

Details for any construction
None

Activity 10:
Find out what soil is made of

Objective
Awareness that soil is made up of different things

Experience
Using water to separate the main constituents of soil

Skills involved
1. Thoroughly mixing soil with water using a measuring cylinder
2. Observing and naming the parts which have separated

Unfamiliar words

Measuring cylinder, contents, humus, clay, sand, gravel, layers, floating, cloudy

Safety points

None

General notes

1. Some help with the observation will be needed.
2. The words humus, clay and gravel will need explanation. Separate displays of humus, clay, sand, gravel and small stones would be useful here.

Apparatus list

Measuring cylinder (preferably not plastic)
Beaker
Soil (a variety of soils from different gardens would be useful)
Stirring rod

Details for any construction

None

Activity 11:
Giving your soil a name

Objective

To appreciate that soils have different names depending on their contents

Experience

Classifying soils with the aid of a flow chart

Skills involved

1. Ability to read instructions
2. Ability to follow directions indicated on flow chart
3. Observation and interpretation

Unfamiliar words

Fertiliser, flow chart, stony, peaty, crumbly, chalky, squeeze, gritting, loam, clayey

Safety points

None

General notes

1. Several different kinds of soils should be investigated by *each* group and results compared.
2. Make sure pupils understand the terminology.

Apparatus list

Samples of different soils labelled A, B, C, etc.
Containers to hold the soil samples

Details for any construction

None

Activity 12:
Looking for animals in soil

Objective

Knowledge that soil contains many kinds of animal life, some harmful to plants and some useful

Experience

Looking for living things in the soil and trying to classify them

Skills involved

1. Observation and the ability to describe what is seen
2. Using a reference guide in order to name the 'animals' found
3. Ability to use a hand lens and simple microscope

Unfamiliar words

Animals, earthworms, humus, container, microscope, complete

Safety points

It would be wise to ask pupils to wash their hands at the end of the Activity.

General notes

It is important that the soil is 'fresh'. Soil from a compost heap should contain many kinds of living things.

Apparatus list

Various samples of soil
Newspaper or plastic trays
A few plant labels (to help turn over the soil)
Various kinds of hand lenses
Simple microscope
50 cm³ or 100 cm³ beakers

Details for any construction

None

Activity 13:
Looking at earthworms in soil

Objective
Appreciation that earthworms perform a useful purpose in the soil

Experience
To make a simple wormery and to find what actions worms have on the soil.

Skills involved
. Preparation of a jam jar 'wormery' according to illustrated instructions
. To make observations and interpret results

Unfamiliar words
Earthworms, layers, anything

Safety points
It would be wise to encourage pupils to wash their hands at the end of this Activity.

General notes
. Make sure that the soil is loamy and damp.
. A little well rotted compost could be mixed with the soil.
. If the jar is placed in a dark cupboard, make sure it is not too near a radiator or the soil may dry out.

Apparatus list
Jam jars (preferably 2 lb)
Soil (moist and loamy)
Chalk
Sand
Worms
A suitable dark area to keep jars for a few days
Some method of labelling the jars in order to identify which group they belong to

Details for any construction
None

Activity 14:
Finding out if crops can be grown in the soil

Objective
Knowledge that the quality of soil can be assessed by the amount of plant material it will grow

Experience
To investigate the quality of the soil by the amount of plant material (mustard seedlings) it will produce

Skills involved
1. Preparing the soil and putting the correct amount of soil in the pot
2. Correct labelling of pots
3. Adding the correct number of seeds
4. Measuring growth of seedlings
5. Ability to observe and record observations on the record sheet
6. Interpreting results and answering questions

Unfamiliar words
Scatter, weigh

Safety points
None

General notes
1. Make sure that there is a wide variation in soil samples.
2. Until the seeds have germinated cover the tops of the pots with glass or plastic sheet and sheets of newspaper. This will conserve the moisture content of the soil. As soon as seed leaves are pushing through the soil remove the glass, give the seedling plenty of light and keep the soil moist.
3. Check that pots have been correctly labelled.
4. See also 'Notes for teacher'.

Apparatus list
Several soil samples
10 cm plant pots or similar plastic containers
Mustard seed
Filter paper

Tin lid
Pairs of scissors
Balance

Details for any construction
None

Activity 15:
Testing soil for nitrogen

Objective
Knowledge of how to test soils for the presence of nitrogen

Experience
Testing various soil samples for the presence of nitrogen

Skills involved
1. Measuring small quantities of solutions, i.e. 1 cm³
2. Following stage by stage instructions
3. Correct method of folding filter paper before placing it in the funnel
4. Comparing coloured solution with coloured chart
5. Recording observations

Unfamiliar words
Filter funnel, filter paper, nitrogen, solution, colour chart, mixture, compare, chemicals

Safety points
Take normal precautions when using chemicals.

General notes
Although the illustrated instructions explain the procedure very clearly, some general discussion regarding the measuring of small quantities and how to compare colours should be carried out before pupils start the Activity.

Apparatus list
3 test tubes
Filter funnel
Filter paper
Nitrogen test solution 1 } See 'Notes for
Nitrogen test solution 2 } teacher'
Cork to fit test tubes
Soil samples
Nitrogen colour charts (supplied by manufacturers of test solutions)

Details for any construction
None

Activity 16:
Testing soil for potash

Objective
Knowledge of how to test soils for the presence of potash

Experience
Testing various soil samples for the presence of potash

Skills involved
See 'Skills involved' for Activity 15

Unfamiliar words
Potash test solution, potash colour chart

Safety points
Take normal precautions when using chemicals.

General notes
1. Remind pupils to refer back to the step by step illustrated instructions given for Activity 15.
2. Some help may be needed regarding colour matching.

Apparatus list
3 test tubes
Cork to fit tubes
Filter funnel
Filter paper
Potash test solution 1 } See 'Notes for
Potash test solution 2 } teacher'
Potash colour chart
Soil samples

Details for any construction
None

Activity 17:
Testing soil for phosphates

Objective
Knowledge of how to test soils for the presence of phosphates

Experience
Testing various soil samples for the presence of phosphates

Skills involved
1. Measuring small quantities of solutions
2. Following stage by stage instructions
3. Scraping the tin rod until shiny and then stirring the solution for 30 seconds
4. Comparing colour of solution with phosphates colour chart
5. Recording observations

Unfamiliar words
Phosphates test solution, tin rod, phosphates colour chart, scrape, compare

Safety points
Take normal precautions when using chemicals.

General notes
Since this is the last soil test it will be necessary to check that the 'Soil chemicals record sheet' (page 32 of pupils' book) is completed, including the last column 'What crops would grow well on this soil'. The results of each group should then be compared, and class discussion should follow.

Apparatus list
3 test tubes
Cork to fit tubes
Filter funnel
Filter paper
Phosphates test solution 1 } See 'Notes for
Phosphates test solution 2 } teacher'
Tin rod
Fine sand paper
Soil samples
Phosphates colour chart

Details for any construction
None

Answers to questions in pupils' book

A letter D indicates that the answer cannot be predicted, usually because it is dependent on the results of the class experiments.

Activity 7
1. So you can wet it evenly and thoroughly
2. To stop the soil falling out or being watered out through the hole(s) in the bottom of the pot

Activity 10
1. 3, 4 or 5
2. Twigs, dead leaves
3. Humus
4. Clay
5. Gravel, stones

Activity 13
1. Worm casts
2. Mixed the layers
3. They mix up top soil and lower layers (subsoil). They take humus down into the soil. They let air into (aerate) the soil.
4. No

DIAGRAM 11. Expected results.

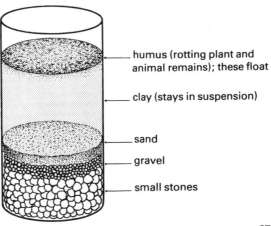

humus (rotting plant and animal remains); these float

clay (stays in suspension)

sand

gravel

small stones

Keeping Going

Summary of contents

This Unit has four sections and is about cars, car drivers and their safety on the road.

The first group of Activities introduces the pupil to the electric circuitry of the car and/or motor cycle, e.g. the wiring of flashing indicators and reversing lights. Car corrosion is also investigated, which includes testing the effectiveness of de-icers and rust stoppers.

The last two sections are concerned with road safety. One section looks at the reflective nature of road signs: why some surfaces are different from others, and what makes a sign reflect. The final section looks at how traffic lights control traffic flow. This leads to an investigation into poor behaviour by some drivers at traffic lights and shows how this behaviour causes accidents.

Equipment list for whole of Unit

To be made

Earth return circuit board (Activity 1)
Leads with 4 mm plugs
Leads with auto connectors   ⎫ (Activities
Leads with crocodile (croc) clips ⎬ 1-4)
Fused car battery connector   ⎭
Reversing light board (Activity 2)
Car flashing indicator board and kit (Activity 3)
Clip boards, for note taking (Activities 5, 14-16)

To be bought or obtained from other departments

Car batteries (12 V)
Auto connectors
Flasher unit, complete with two lamps
Switch (single pole, two way)
Dashboard warning light
Car reflectors

Selection of rust stoppers
Anti-freeze
De-icers
Paraffin
Iron flasks for freezing (Scientific apparatus suppliers)
Small paint brushes

To be collected

An old car (not absolutely necessary, but desirable)
Jars or assorted glass containers
2'' nails
Tin cans
Plastic teaspoons
Reflective sign and other road sign material (try Highways Department, Local Council)
Cat's eyes
Glass marbles
Cardboard tubes

Assumed normally available in laboratory

Lamps (bayonet, 12 V; 21 W vehicle lamps)
Beakers
Bunsen burners
Tripods
Gauze squares
Metal tongs
Plastic bowls (or similar containers)
Thermometers
Test tubes and racks
Hand torch
Hand magnifiers
Stop watch
Glass prism
A few tools (pliers, hacksaw, screwdrivers, wire strippers, soldering iron, solder, files)
Emery cloth
Cardboard
Salt
Chinagraph pencils
Access to slide projector
Access to refrigerator (to make ice)

Forward planner

Activity number	Advanced planning needed	Approximate Activity time (40 min period)	Are results of a previous Activity necessary?
1	None*	1 period	No
2	None*	2 periods	Activity 1
3	None*	2 periods	Activity 1 (possibly 2)
4	None*	2 periods	Activity 3
5	Arrange access to a rusty car, e.g. staff car park. Otherwise arrange visit to local scrap yard	2 periods (may be less depending on car and location)	No
6	None	2 single periods separated by about one week	No
7	None	2 periods (setting up) + 1 period the following week to conclude	No
8	Make ice	2 periods	No
9	None	15 min in one lesson + 25 min in a later one	No
10	None	15 min in one lesson + 25 min in a later one	No
11	None	2 periods	No
12	None	1 period	No
13	None	1 period + 1 period (approx) for discussion	Activity 12 desirable
14	} Obtain consent forms for pupils	2 double periods or 1 triple + 1 single+	No
15		2 double periods + 1 single period +	No
16		3 periods +	No

+ These times are estimates due to the external factors which must be present.
* Assumes that apparatus for these Activities has been made.

Notes for teacher

From the summary of the Unit you will see that the contents fall roughly into four sections: (a) car circuitry, (b) effectiveness of de-icers and ruster stoppers, (c) road signs and their reflective nature and (d) traffic lights and the behaviour of drivers when crossing lights.

Activities 1-4 (car circuitry)
These circuits allow the pupil to experience the wiring together of actual car accessories and to become aware that the car body itself acts as a conductor. It is hoped that the pupils will be allowed time to think their way through the Activities instead of being given a simple recipe type experiment.

Activities 5-11 (the problems of ice and corrosion)
It is important when pupils are using materials concerned with these Activities that normal safety precautions are taken. If pupils have difficulty in reading the manufacturers' instructions on the container then it may be advisable to provide a supplementary sheet which gives the instructions in simpler

language. However, this method should only be used as a last resort since it is good training for pupils to find and read the maker's instructions before attempting to use the materials. Discourage the attitude that if everything else fails, then read the instructions!

If time permits it may be a good idea to allow some pupils to carry out an independent investigation by interviewing car owners to find out what rust stoppers they have found to be effective and then to compare these results with the results from their own experiments.

Activities 12 and 13 (road signs)

The signs which the pupils will be handling must be properly labelled: (a) reflective sign, (b) standard sign or (c) translucent sign. When discussing the merits of each kind of sign it may be useful to bear in mind the following points:

1. Reflective signs would not stand out against the bright background of towns and cities. Electricity supplies are to hand, therefore translucent signs would be more effective.
2. Reflective signs would be more appropriate in country districts where the electricity supply is not so easily available and where reflective signs are effective and economical.

Possible follow-up work could involve a survey of local signs to find out the types used in a particular locality. Also work on 'visual acuity' and 'reaction times' could be added as supplementary Activities.

Activities 14-16 (traffic lights)

In carrying out these Activities many pupils will be working outside the school. It is therefore important that they are well briefed regarding the salient points of the exercise.

A reasonable time must be allowed for discussion on the results and on the best way to present them. There is a strong link here with mathematics and since pictorial representation, in some form or other, makes the understanding of results easier, some form of graph should be attempted. Results must be *interpreted* if they are to make sense.

Main objectives and ideas

Main objectives
1. Awareness that what appears to be complex wiring on cars is made up of simple units
2. Development of skills and confidence relating to simple wiring in cars
3. Knowledge of causes and preventions that can be taken regarding rusting on cars
4. Realisation of the need to choose the *most suitable* of a number of different strategies
5. Knowledge that irresponsible driving can endanger people's lives

Key ideas
1. A car body can act as an earth return
2. Adaptability of simple circuits in real situations
3. Causes, effects and treatment of rust
4. Selection of the right de-icer for the job in hand
5. The damage that can be caused by water freezing
6. How reflection can save lives
7. Traffic lights are programmed to do a certain job rather than just go on and off
8. Driver training does pay off

Relevant information
1. Department of the Environment *Highway Code* (H.M.S.O.)
2. Automobile Association *Book of the Car* (1976)

Information for each Activity

Activity 1:
Simple car circuits

Objectives
1. Knowledge that a car body can act as an earth return
2. Knowledge of parallel circuits

Experience

That by using the car body as an earth return, wiring can be done more economically

Skills involved

1. Connecting circuits using 4 mm plugs and sockets and auto connectors
2. Selecting appropriate leads (choosing the most economical length)

Unfamiliar words

Circuits, parallel, electricity, electrical

Safety points

Use the fused car battery connector

General notes

There are two sets of leads, long leads and short leads. When the circuit board is presented to the pupils the six *long* leads should be connected as shown in the diagram in the pupils' book. The main idea of the Activity is for the pupils to think out the most economical way to rewire the circuit.

Apparatus list

Earth return circuit board
3 long leads with 4 mm plugs
3 short leads with 4 mm plugs
3 long leads with auto connectors
2 short leads with auto connectors
   See diagram 12, page 79, for lengths of leads
2 battery leads, one with a 4 mm plug and an auto plug and the other with two 4 mm plugs
Car battery (12 V)
Fused car battery connector
3 lamps (12 V)
Pliers

Details for any construction
See diagram 12, page 79, for construction of the earth return board, and diagram 13, page 80, for the fused car battery connector.

Activity 2:
Wiring up a car reversing lamp

Objective

Familiarisation with simple car circuit

Experiences

1. Using real car components to make electrical circuits
2. Designing a suitable circuit so that all parts function correctly

Skills involved

1. Ability to manipulate electrical car components
2. Ability to relate the actual components to the drawings in the diagram

Unfamiliar words

Reversing, dashboard

Safety points

Use the fused car battery connector.

General notes

1. Remove bulb from the reversing lamp before handing to pupils.
2. The use of a pair of pliers may facilitate the joining of the auto connectors.
3. An extension to the Activity could be an investigation into what happens if one of the two bulbs fuses. This may help the pupils to appreciate how satisfactory this circuit is as 'an information giver'.

Apparatus list

Reversing light board (complete)
4 long leads
Short lead
Auto connector socket
Car battery
Fused car battery connector

Details for any construction
See diagram in pupils' book, page 3, for construction of the reversing light board. Suggested dimensions for the board are 38 cm by 12 cm. The metal strip should be brass and measure about 33 cm long and 2.5 cm wide. One lead from the reversing lamp should have a 4 mm plug on it, and the other should have a bullet connector. The other leads should have crocodile clips on one end and either 4 mm plugs or bullet connectors on the other end.

See diagram 13, page 80, for the construction of the fused car battery connector.

Activity 3:
Making a car flashing indicator circuit

Objectives
1. Familiarisation with more complex forms of car circuitry
2. To develop confidence to use previously gained knowledge in order to solve more complex problems

Experience
How to wire a flashing indicator circuit

Skills involved
1. To follow sequential instructions
2. To check work done by referring to a diagram
3. Ability to assess that the completed circuit functions correctly

Unfamiliar words
Indicator, flasher unit, terminal

Safety points
Use the fused car battery connector.

General notes
The flasher unit on the board has three terminals: 'B' has a brown lead attached to it and is for connecting to the battery (positive or negative terminal); 'L' has a red lead attached to it and is for connecting to the lamps; 'P' is for connecting to the final bulb. The wires are colour coded only to help the pupil with the wiring.

Apparatus list
Car flashing indicator board (complete)
5 bulbs (12 V, 21 W or 24 W)
2 croc — croc leads (blue wire) 20 cm
2 croc — croc leads (red wire) 20 cm
1 croc — auto spade lead (black wire) 20 cm
Switch unit
1 lead, 4 mm plug — auto spade, about
    ½ metre long
Car battery
Fused car battery connector

Details for any construction
See diagram 14, page 81 , for construction of the car flashing indicator board, switch unit

and modified lamp holder. Please refer to the diagrams on pages 5-7 of the pupils' book for assembly of the entire board.
See diagram 13, page 80 , for the construction of the fused car battery connector.

Activity 4:
Wiring a car flashing indicator circuit

Objective
To use ideas gained from a previous Activity and apply them to a similar situation

Experience
To wire a car flashing indicator circuit using all the relevant car components

Skills involved
1 To follow a logical pattern of wiring
2. To be able to use a soldering iron (A crimping tool can sometimes be used instead.)
3. To recognise all the parts used in the circuit

Unfamiliar words
Coil

Safety points
1. If pupils are using soldering irons they must be connected through an isolating transformer or covered with a heat resistant sleeve.
2. Use the fused car battery connector.
3. Emphasise to the pupil that the car battery is the last part of the circuit to be connected.

General notes
Allow adequate time for pupils to complete the wiring, but intervention may be necessary if there is a danger of frustration and deterioration of interest.

Apparatus list
Car battery
Fused car battery connector
Flasher unit complete with 2 lamps (as used on motor cycles)

Switch (single pole, two way)
Dashboard warning light complete with holder
Some wires
Some push-on connectors for the wires
A few tools (small screwdrivers, pliers, wire
  strippers, soldering iron, solder)

Details for any construction
None

Activity 5:
What metals are cars made of?

Objectives
1. Awareness that cars rust
2. Awareness that preventative measures are
   taken by manufacturers

Experiences
1. To discover that a car is made up of several
   kinds of material, some of which are more
   susceptible to rust than others
2. The kind of rust preventative measures that
   have been taken by manufacturers

Skills involved
Observation and careful recording

Unfamiliar words
Engine block, fibre glass, steel, cast iron,
chrome, aluminium

Safety points
1. Pupils should not be allowed to crawl
   underneath vehicles.
2. They should not be allowed to interfere
   with car controls.
3. Ensure that metal objects are kept away
   from battery terminals.
4. Do not allow naked lights of any kind near
   the car.

General notes
It is very important that appropriate
supervisory precautions are taken.

Apparatus list
An old car
Clip board for note taking

Details for any construction
None

Activity 6:
What makes steel rust?

Objective
To identify the causes of rusting

Experience
That for iron to rust certain factors must be
present

Skills involved
1. Careful setting up and labelling of bottles
2. Observing and interpreting results

Unfamiliar words
Corrosion, shiny, oxygen, paraffin

Safety points
1. Extinguish all flames before using paraffin.
2. Hand out only small quantities of paraffin.

General notes
Make sure that pupils pour the boiled water
into the jar or wide mouthed bottle carefully in
order to avoid air bubbles getting into the
water. The reason for this may have to be
explained.

Apparatus list
4 jars or similar containers
4 cardbaord or plastic covers for the jars
16 2'' nails (cleaned with emery cloth)
Paraffin
Salt
Chinagraph pencil
Bunsen burner
Tripod   } to prepare freshly
Beaker   } boiled tap water
Beaker tongs   }

Details for any construction
None

Activity 7:
Do 'rust stoppers' work?

Objective
To investigate the claim that corrosion can be
treated

Experiences
1. That certain proprietary substances can be used to treat and/or prevent rusting
2. That some of these substances are more effective than others

Skills involved
1. Preparing the tin can by filing
2. Applying the rust stopper according to manufacturers' instructions
3. Observation and careful recording

Unfamiliar words
Chrome, dangerous, instructions

Safety points
1. Pupils must wear safety goggles and some form of protective clothing.
2. Make sure that pupils are aware of the dangers of these substances.
3. Make sure that there are adequate first aid materials to hand should an accident occur.

General notes
With some pupils it may be useful to discuss cathodic protection or to set this up as a demonstration experiment.

Apparatus list
Some clean newly emptied tin cans
File
Selection of rust stoppers (about four or five)
Plastic bowl plus water
Salt
Some small paint brushes
Chinagraph pencil

Details for any construction
None

Activity 8:
How hot is melting ice?

Objective
Awareness that certain chemicals when added to water can cause a lowering of the freezing point

Experience
That mixtures containing water and anti-freeze have a lower freezing point than water alone

Skills involved
1. Careful use of thermometer
2. Ability to read thermometer scales
3. Ability to measure specified quantities

Unfamiliar words
Anti-freeze, freezing point, de-icer, thermometer, temperature

Safety points
1. Goggles should always be worn when pouring and using anti-freeze.
2. The anti-freeze should be kept in a dark glass bottle, clearly labelled.

General notes
Ice will be needed for this Activity.

Apparatus list
Bunsen burner
Tripod
Gauze
Thermometer
Salt
Anti-freeze
100 cm³ beaker
Crushed ice
Teaspoon (plastic)

Details for any construction
None

Activity 9:
How de-icers work

Objective
To investigate the claim that de-icers prevent water freezing

Experience
That under normal climatic conditions de-icers (anti-freeze) will prevent water freezing solid

Skills involved
1. Careful handling of materials
2. Preparation of solution to go into test tubes
3. Correct labelling of tubes
4. Observation and recording

Unfamiliar words
Freezing compartment

Safety points
1. Pupils must use safety goggles.
2. Make sure that de-icer is well labelled and in a dark bottle.
3. Test tubes must be well secured when placed in the refrigerator.

General notes
It may be interesting to discuss with the class what drivers had to do years ago before anti-freeze was obtainable.

Apparatus list
Availability of a refrigerator
3 test tubes in rack or stand
Chinagraph pencil
De-icers (salt and anti-freeze)

Details for any construction
None

Activity 10:
Do de-icers harm cars?

Objective
To investigate whether de-icers have any side effects on the parts that they come into contact with

Experience
That some de-icing substances have a corrosive effect on car bodies

Skills involved
1. Setting up the materials for the experiment
2. Careful observation
3. Interpreting results

Unfamiliar words
Complain!

Safety points
Goggles should always be worn when pouring and using anti-freeze.

General notes
1. Any precautions stated on the anti-freeze label must be made known to the class.
2. Anti-freeze can sometimes inhibit rust formation.

Apparatus list
3 test tubes (with corks) in rack
3 clean iron nails

De-icers (anti-freeze and salt)
Chinagraph pencil
Spatula or plastic teaspoon
Details for any construction
None

Activity 11:
When water freezes...

Objective
To investigate the effects of extreme temperatures on anti-freeze when used in a closed container

Experience
That under extreme conditions of temperature anti-freeze does work

Skills involved
1. To make up the correct anti-freeze mixture
2. Some manipulation in preparing the iron flasks for freezing
3. Careful observation and interpretation of results

Unfamiliar words
Expansion

Safety points
1. Pupils must wear safety goggles when using anti-freeze.
2. Care must be taken when uncapping the iron flask.
3. Put beakers containing iron flasks in a safe place.

General notes
1. Make sure that the iron containers are full of liquid before finally tightening the screw cap.
2. The cylinder containing anti-freeze should not burst.

Apparatus list
2 iron flasks for freezing (see scientific apparatus suppliers' catalogue)
Anti-freeze
Small spanner to fit bolt head on iron flasks
Rack of test tubes
Beaker
Salt
Crushed ice

Details for any construction
None

Activity 12:
Traffic sign surfaces

Objective
Appreciation of the nature of reflective surfaces and their functional application

Experience
That different road sign surfaces reflect light in different ways

Skills involved
Ability to recognise differences in the surfaces of road signs

Unfamiliar words
Reflective, reflection, beam of light, translucent

Safety points
If a mains projector is used as a light source make sure that all connections are safe

General notes
See 'Notes for teacher' for suggestions for further Activities

Apparatus list
Different kinds of road sign material (reflective signs, standard signs, translucent signs — these should be labelled for recognition purposes)
Cardboard tube
Torch or projector for light source

Details for any construction
Broken road signs may be obtained from the Highways Department of many local councils. They would have to be cut to a suitable size

Activity 13:
What makes signs reflect?

Objective
To find out what attributes make a good road sign

Experience
That light is reflected in different ways from different surfaces

Skills involved
1. Manipulation and alignment of light source, reflector and cardboard tube
2. Selecting order of brightness
3. Recording and interpretation of results

Unfamiliar words
Prism, cat's eyes, reflector

Safety points
None

General notes
Since a little difficulty may be encountered in ordering 'brightness' it may be a useful exercise to compare group results with a general class result. A block or bar graph may be used with advantage here.

Apparatus list
Glass prism
Car reflectors
Cat's eyes
Glass marble
Sign surfaces (as used in Activity 12)
Torch or apparatus to give a similar source of light
Cardboard tube
Hacksaw
Magnifying glass

Details for any construction
None

Activity 14:
How do traffic lights work?

Objectives
Appreciation of the significance of traffic light control and of the fact that they work to a pattern designed to suit traffic requirements

Experience
Checking time sequences at traffic lights

Skills involved
1. Using a stop watch

2. Observing and recording according to given criteria
3. Interpretation of results

Unfamiliar words
Sequence, controlling

Safety points
1. Safety aspects here need special consideration.
2. It would be prudent to make use of consent forms.
3. Unsupervised pupils working outside school should not exceed three in number.

General notes
It may be worth considering the construction and operation of four sets of traffic lights as a part class Activity. These could be made while the more trustworthy pupils are out of school investigating the traffic light sequences. Later these traffic light models could be used as a class demonstration using the results of the investigations.

Apparatus list
Stop watch
Clip board and pencil

Details for any construction
None, unless a model traffic light system is constructed

Activity 15:
What do drivers do at traffic lights?

Objective
To investigate the behaviour of drivers at traffic lights

Experience
That many drivers disregard the light sequence at traffic lights

Skills involved
Careful counting and recording for an exact time interval, as part of a team effort

Unfamiliar words
'Jumping' the lights

Safety points
See 'Safety points' for Activity 14

General notes
See 'Notes for teacher'.

Apparatus list
Clip board and pencil

Details for any construction
None

Activity 16:
What happens when drivers 'jump' the lights

Objective
Awareness that car accidents are related to drivers' behaviour

Experience
That car accidents or near accidents can be caused by disregarding safety regulations

Skills involved
Careful counting and recording for an exact time interval, as part of a team effort

Unfamiliar words
Accident, behaviour

Safety points
See 'Safety points' for Activity 14.

General notes
See 'General notes' for Activity 14.

Apparatus list
Clip board and pencil

Details for any construction
None

Answers to questions in pupils' book

A letter D indicates that the answer cannot be predicted, usually because it is dependent on the results of the class experiments.

Activity 1
1. The metal strip
2. The metal car body
3. An extra return or earth wire is needed

Activity 2
What to do
6. Through the metal car body
8. Yes; No
10. So that he/she will know when the reversing light is on
Questions
1. As soon as the car's reverse gear is disengaged, the reversing light goes out automatically.
2. (a) So that the driver can see behind in the dark
   (b) To warn others that the car is reversing
3. The metal bodywork

Activity 3
What to do
4. The bulb flashes.
5. Yes
7. The flashing indicator switch
9. Yes; Yes; In the middle; To supply current to the repeater indicator on the dashboard when either pair of flashers is used

Activity 5
What to do

1.

Car body	forms a strong light cage	steel
Engine block	forms rigid base for moving parts	cast iron
Electric wires	conduct electricity	copper
Terminals on battery	conduct heavy currents	lead

2.

Steel	rusting right through	
Cast iron	only slight surface rust	
Copper	little change	
Lead	little change	

3. (a) Painted
   (b) Chromed
   (c) Painted or untreated
4. Lead terminals, copper wires and possibly engine block were not treated because they do not rust much.
5. 1. Wings
   2. Sills
   3. Door bottoms
   4. Underbody
   5. Headlamp surrounds
6. They are exposed to: water, salt, stone chips.
7. Fibreglass or aluminium

Activity 6
1.

Jars	A	B	C	D
Air				✓
Paraffin				
Water	✓	✓	✓	
Salt		✓		
Oxygen	✓	✓		✓
Did the nails rust?	slightly	a lot	no	no

2. Water and oxygen
3. Salt
4. Paint, keeps water and salt out; Chrome, keeps water and salt out; Zinc plate, allows iron to combine with a material other than oxygen

Activity 7
1, 2. D
3. No
4. It protects the steel from water and oxygen.
5. Bumpers, wheel discs, backs of mirrors, reflectors behind headlamps bulbs, door handles

Activity 8
2. D
3. 0°C
5. D
6. It melts. Less than 0°C.
8. D
9. The ice melts. Less than 0°C
10. 0°C. D. D. They reduce it.

Activity 9
What to do
5. A   Solid ice; test tube broken
   B   Unfrozen or lightly frozen
   C   Mushy ice
Questions
1. D
2. Anti-freeze
3. Anti-freeze
4. It would make it rust.

Activity 10
1. Salt water
2. It causes rust.
3. It rusts their car bodies.
4. It would run off the road and would cost too much.

Activity 11
1. Burst it.
2. It would burst the radiator or engine block.
3. Anti-freeze

Activity 12
What to do
1. Reflect it
2. No
3. D. On a lonely country road, because it is darker there. The sign reflects the light from the car's headlights.
4. By internal illumination. You can see the light behind it. It is passing straight through.
    (a) In town, signs have to 'compete' with many other bright lights.
    (b) In the country there is no power supply and no need for the added running costs.

Activity 14
Questions: page 26
1. D. If not, the roads do not carry the same flow of traffic.
2. No
3. Amber
4. To give cars time to stop
Questions: page 27
1. To allow pedestrians to cross
2. A matter of opinion

Activity 15
1, 2. D
3. Drivers are warned to expect the red light by the amber one. People think of the colour red as indicating danger. When their lights are red it is more likely that lights for traffic going the other way are green.
4. Because they are already on the move and it is easier to keep going than to stop.

Activity 16
1. a
2. These results are not so obvious as actual accidents.
3.4. D
5. No. Drivers would stop too suddenly and skid (tie in with *Starting and Stopping*).
6. Prepare to go. Stop if it is safe to do so.
7. By making other drivers annoyed and bad tempered

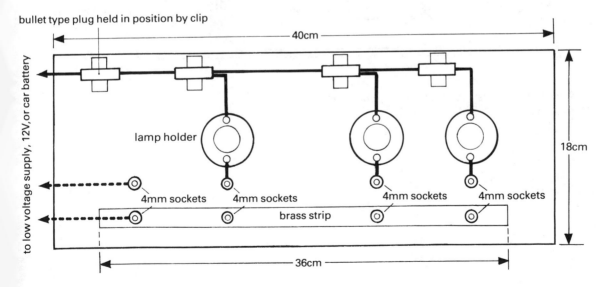

DIAGRAM 12. Construction of earth return circuit board (Activity 1).

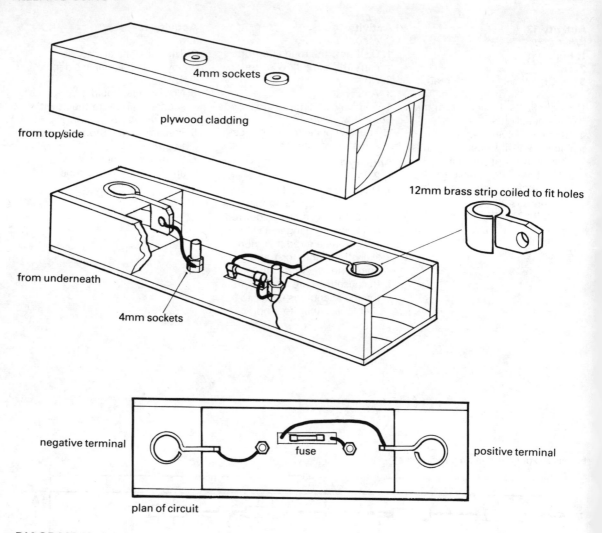

4mm sockets

plywood cladding

from top/side

from underneath

4mm sockets

12mm brass strip coiled to fit holes

negative terminal

fuse

positive terminal

plan of circuit

DIAGRAM 13. Construction of fused car battery connector (Activities 1-4).

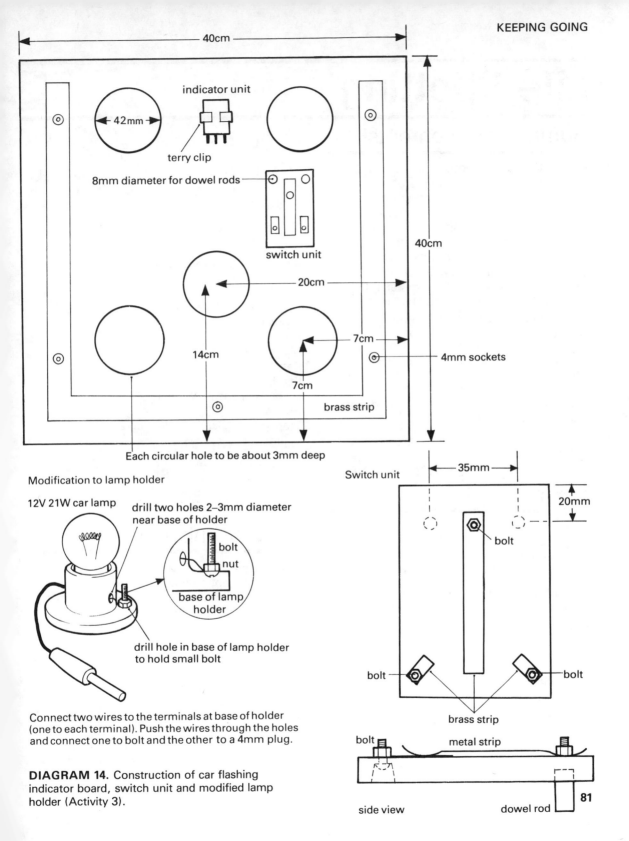

indicator unit

terry clip

42mm

8mm diameter for dowel rods

switch unit

40cm

20cm

14cm

7cm

7cm

4mm sockets

brass strip

Each circular hole to be about 3mm deep

Modification to lamp holder

12V 21W car lamp

drill two holes 2–3mm diameter near base of holder

bolt
nut
base of lamp holder

drill hole in base of lamp holder to hold small bolt

Connect two wires to the terminals at base of holder (one to each terminal). Push the wires through the holes and connect one to bolt and the other to a 4mm plug.

DIAGRAM 14. Construction of car flashing indicator board, switch unit and modified lamp holder (Activity 3).

Switch unit

35mm

20mm

bolt

bolt

bolt

brass strip

bolt

metal strip

side view

dowel rod

81

Life Spotting

Summary of contents

The Unit's main purpose is to encourage pupils to take an interest in the ecology of their local environment, whether urban or rural, wild or derelict, parks or playing fields, or even on the school site itself.

The Unit is generously illustrated with drawings of plants and insects; it provides easy to follow animal keys and plant charts to help with identification of specimens. Several methods of carrying out investigations into plant and animal distributions are clearly explained.

The last two Activities in the Unit attempt to encourage pupils to make decisions about what they would do to improve their local environments, bearing in mind that provision should be made to safeguard our wild plants, animals and bird life.

Equipment list for whole of Unit

To be made
Tulgren funnels (Activity 4)
Possibly pooters (Activity 4)
Quadrat frames (Activities 5 and 7)

To be bought or obtained from other departments
Cameras
Films
Silva compass (from local scout shops)
20 m tapes
7 mm diameter dowel
6 mm diameter and 8 mm diameter plastic tubing
Large plastic funnels
Perforated zinc sheet
Plant identification books, e.g. *Collins Pocket Guide to Wild Flowers* by D. McClintock and R.S.R. Fitter, *Trees and Shrubs in Wood and Hedgerow* by H. Vedel and J. Lange (Methuen); many books in the Blandford series

To be collected
2 metal tent pegs

Assumed normally available in laboratory
Collecting tubes
Hand lenses
Dishes or small bowls
Trowels
Polythene bags
Microscope
Petri dishes
Clip boards
Coloured pencils or pens
Rulers
Transparent plastic bottles or jars (approx 50 cm³)

Forward planner

All Units
Before attempting any of the Activities in this Unit, careful advanced planning is necessary. In a town you may find that the school site or some adjacent wasteland is adequate, but if you intend to use nature reserves or farm land, it is important to write early for permission.

It is not necessary to carry out the Activities in numerical order except for those which teach a particular technique, e.g. using a camera, using a magnetic compass, using keys, etc. However, when pupils are studying a particular area the related Activities will require more than one session. This is indicated where necessary.

Forward planner

Activity number	Advanced planning needed	Approximate Activity time (40 min period)	Are results of a previous Activity necessary?
1	Make sure that you have adequate cameras and that they are properly loaded (encourage pupils to bring their own if possible)	2 periods	No
2	Collect the 12 plants illustrated on the plant chart for display	2-3 periods, depending on proximity of site and number of groups involved	No
3	Collect animals the previous day — garden compost is a good source	2 periods	No
4	Make sure that you have plenty of material including pooters and Tulgren funnels. Allow 2-3 days to collect insects from funnels	2 periods using pooters and identifying + 2 periods to identify soil animals from Tulgren funnels	Should follow Activity 3 (can be combined with Activities 1, 5 and 7 for a longer study)
5	Make sure you have an adequate number of quadrats (these may have to be made)	1 period for 'throws' + 1 period for entering up results	Activity 2 (can be combined with Acties 1, 4 and 7 for a longer study)
6	Find an area with varying features, e.g. rough ground, path, a stream (if possible), small hedge, low wall, etc.	2 periods, depending on number of groups and location of site	Activity 2
7	Make sure that you have an adequate number of quadrats and 20 m tapes	2-3 periods (preferably ½ day excursion on a field trip)	Activity 2 and preferably Activities 5 and 6
8	Arrange to visit suitable site — park or public gardens, etc. (could set for homework)	2-3 periods, depending on location of site	No
9	Arrange to visit suitable site (could set for homework)	2 periods	No

Notes for teacher

Because the sites that a school is able to study will vary, the Activities in this Unit can be applied in many ways. It is not intended that schools should spend time and money travelling long distances to big nature reserves, but rather to use small sites near the school or in the school grounds, so that the work can be done in lesson time. Of course, if there is the time and money, it is nice to take a day or half a day to study a contrasting area. However, this Unit was designed primarily for schools and pupils for whom such a visit would not be possible.

When selecting sites to study, see if it is necessary to obtain permission from an owner first and make sure the area is safe. Areas with broken glass or old rubbish tips are obviously not suitable. Extra safety precautions have to be taken near water.

Only Activities 2 and 3 are 'once only' exercises. The others may be done once, more than once or not at all, depending on the area. If photographs are taken wherever possible and clean copies of the results are kept, these can be combined into a wall chart for display when the Unit is finished (see 'Projects' below).

Activities 1, 4, 5 and 7 can be combined to form a larger project. With some classes different groups can work on different Activites.

It is important to obtain sufficient equipment for the class to work in small groups, preferably not more than two pupils. This will probably mean borrowing extra 20 m tapes.

Most of the record sheets (printed in the pupils' books and also available as record sheet masters) are for plants only. If animals are collected and studied use the extra blank lines to record them.

Activity 1

Using a Silva compass means one can take repeat photographs at other times. The Silva compass can also be used to record the direction of line and belt studies (see Activities 6 and 7).

Activity 2

It is not vital to identify every plant. If pupils learn some of the names they will be able to do the rest of the exercises in the Unit. The chart is designed to make the pupils look carefully.

Activity 3

The animal keys can also be used for Activity 12 in *Grow Your Own*.

Activity 4

This is usually a popular Activity. Each specimen should be put into a separate collecting box, because many of these animals are carnivores. The pooters are easy to make and use. Plastic or polythene bottles are better than glass, but boiling tubes can be used. Tulgren funnels are easily made from a large plastic funnel (the size used for brewing) with a circle of perforated zinc inside. Any light source can be used. It is best to have a bank of about 10 Tulgren funnels.

Activity 5

The quadrats are very cheap to make so there should be sufficient for one between two. Then one pupil observes and calls out while the other records. Quadrats are used to compare vegetation. Pupils can do one set of throws on a frequently mown lawn, and another on wasteland and then compare the results.

It may not be possible to identify every plant, but try to have an identification book available. This Activity can be used as a preparation for Activity 7.

Activity 6

The line will be most interesting if it crosses a path, stream or hedge which will cause the vegetation to change. Ideally there should be one tape between two. In a very interesting area, the tape can be moved along and a continuous line can be recorded.

Activity 7

This is a good way to study vegetation across an area. Animals can also be recorded quadrat by quadrat. If you decide to make this a big project, use Activities 4, 5 and 6 to practise. The example in the pupils' book has a chart prepared from a record sheet. These records were taken across a narrow path, the vegetation at the sides being different from that in the centre. Good sites to choose are (a) across a path, (b) across a small stream, (c) across a hedge, or (d) starting from a stream or hedge and recording away from it.

Activity 8

This Activity was designed to be carried out in a park or school grounds. It encourages pupils to be aware both of wild and cultivated areas. It makes a good homework or individual project.

Activity 9

This is to help pupils realise that often the activities of man help wild life. It is also a good homework project or a suitable Activity for bad weather, when the school building can be used as the subject and the work can be done with minimum time spent outdoors.

Projects

Several Activities can be combined into a larger project, and two suggestions for this are given below.

1. The most interesting sites to study are those crossed by a natural or man-made feature such as a river, path, fence or hedge, which will create changes in the vegetation in and around it.

    The following Activities can be used for practice: 2, 3, 5, 6.

    The following Activities then form the study itself: 4, 7. Pupils should make neat lists of their findings and, if possible, examine the insects in each quadrat also.

    Encourage pupils to think of reasons for variation in the plant life. These will include the following:

(a) Many plants will not grow where land is trampled, grazed or mown whereas others grow best under such conditions because plants that might compete with them are eliminated.

(b) Some plants die if their leaves are cut or bruised; others such as grass not only withstand this but are actually stimulated to grow by it.

(c) Some plants cannot grow with their roots in waterlogged soil; others cannot grow in drier areas.

(d) Light and shade, and temperature are very important factors for the growth of many plants.

2. In the absence of a suitable site for 1 above, two different, separate sites can be chosen. Even a simple comparison between a playing field and a lawn can yield interesting results.

    For this project the following Activities can be used for practice: 2, 3.

    The following Activities then form the project itself: 1, 4, 5, 6. Each should be done on the two areas.

    Again pupils should consider reasons for the variations. As well as those in 1 above there may be other factors since two separate areas have been studied. These include:

(a) One area may have had fertiliser applied, or the two may have been treated with different fertilisers.

(b) One may be nearer to a busy road or other source of pollution.

The class results can be made into a wall chart which encourages pupils to lay out their findings and thoughts neatly and logically. Chart 1, page 91, shows a suggested layout for the results of project 1 above, and chart 2, page 91, shows the same for project 2.

Main objectives and ideas

Main objectives
1. To enable pupils to see the diversity of life which is to be found even on small areas of wasteland
2. To encourage pupils to take an interest in local ecology
3. To help pupils to study the ecology of local areas

Key ideas
1. That if results are to be worthwhile, keen observation and accurate recording are essential
2. Awareness of the variety of life that exists in a local environment
3. The effect that man has on the life around him

Relevant information
1. Local National Trusts — help with finding suitable study sites
2. Royal Society for the Protection of Birds — useful literature
3. Environment Studies Association — useful information
4. National Conservancy Council — useful information
5. BBC Horizon Films — could be borrowed
6. *Guide to Field Biology* by J. Sankey (Longman)
7. *Collins Pocket Guide to Wild Flowers* by D. McClintock and R.S.R. Fitter (Collins) — plant identification book
8. *Trees and Shrubs in Wood and Hedgerow* by H. Vedel and J. Lange (Methuen) — plant identification book

Information for each Activity

Activity 1:
Photographic records

Objective
Appreciation that a quick and easy way of keeping a record is to take a photograph

Experience
Using a camera and compass as a means of recording places of particular ecological interest

Skills involved
1. Using a camera
2. Using a compass
3. Reading a compass and recording data
4. Making a photographic record

Unfamiliar words
Photographic, exactly, camera, direction, instructions, compass, needle, arrow, dial, base plate, photograph

Safety points
Take normal precautions applicable to visits outside school, e.g. parental consent forms, pupils to be well briefed beforehand, teacher to visit area before if possible, pupil:teacher ratio to be compatible with local regulations.

General notes
1. Make sure that pupils understand how to use the camera (do not use complicated ones) and compass (much practice will be needed before they are taken on location).
2. It is also important that pupils know exactly how to fill in the record sheets.

Apparatus list
Camera (loaded) e.g. instamatic type
Spare films
Record sheet (It is useful to have this under a plastic cover, backed with a piece of hardboard and held together with a bulldog clip)

Compass (Silva)
Pen or pencil

Details for any construction
None

Activity 2:
Find 12 common plants

Objective
Ability to identify common wasteland plants

Experience
To visit an area of wasteland to attempt to find and identify, with the aid of drawings, the plants named on the record sheet

Skills involved
1. To study the plants on the plant identification sheets and to associate the name of each plant with its drawing
2. Ability to identify the living plants with the drawings
3. Recording observations

Unfamiliar words
Tape measure, wasteland, measure, extra, the twelve plant names

Safety points
Take the same precautions as for Activity 1.

General notes
Pupils should be allowed to see and handle common plants before any attempt is made to visit wasteland. A display of clearly labelled plants in the laboratory would help pupils to become familiar with the plants and their names.

Apparatus list
Plant identification sheets (from pupils' book)
Note book
Record sheet
Tape measure
Pen or pencil

Details for any construction
None

Activity 3:
Animal keys

Objective
To encourage the use of keys to identify and name animals and plants

Experience
Using the animal keys provided to identify and name the animals illustrated

Skills involved
1. Reading and understanding the words, phrases and sentences in the key
2. Following step by step instructions

Unfamiliar words
Animal keys, segments, pairs, insect larvae, saddle, difficulties

Safety points
None

General notes
An overhead transparency of the animal key would be useful to show the class how to use the key. Many pupils will need a great deal of practice with the key before they are able to use it for general identification.

Apparatus list
Animal key (from pupils' book)
Hand lens
Animals to name

Details for any construction
None

Activity 4:
Small animal hunting!

Objective
Knowledge of the method of collecting small animals, i.e. insects

Experience
Using a pooter and Tulgren funnel to collect insects

Skills involved
1. Understanding how the pooter works
2. Using the pooter correctly
3. Transferring insects from the pooter into the collecting tubes
4. Understanding how the Tulgren funnel works and how to use it
5. Identifying and naming insects with the help of the key provided

Unfamiliar words
Probably, microscope, pooter, collecting tubes, Tulgren funnel, trowel, petri dish, insects, beetles, gauze, catching tube, litter

Safety points
Make sure that the mains 60 W lamp is securely supported and is electrically safe.

General notes
It is best if there are two pooters and one Tulgren funnel per group. This Activity demands the ability to carry out techniques which need care and thought. Make sure the skills have been taught before allowing pupils freedom to investigate.

Apparatus list
Pooter
Collecting tubes (small screw top jars — plastic are best)
Hand lens
Tulgren funnel
2 dishes or small bowls
Trowel (garden type)
Polythene bag
Animal key (from pupils' book)
Simple microscope
Petri dish

Details for any construction
Tulgren funnels can be made by using plastic funnels, as used for brewing, and some perforated gauze to put near the bottom of funnel (See diagram 16, page 91).

Pooters can be made from transparent plastic bottles or jars (approx. 50 cm³ size) with screw caps that should be about 25 mm diameter, or two-holed bungs to fit, as shown on page 10 of pupils' book. Two lengths of tubing about 6 mm diameter and 16 cm long are inserted through holes in the lid. They should be a tight fit. Make sure the nylon gauze covers the end of the tube that will be placed in the mouth.

Activity 5:
Using quadrats

Objective
To acquire a knowledge of how to obtain random samples using a quadrat frame

Experience
Using a quadrat to obtain samples of plant species in a given area

Skills involved
1. Using a quadrat frame
2. Identifying plant species in each quadrat 'throw'
3. Recording observations on the quadrat record sheet

Unfamiliar words
Quadrat, measure, sample, random samples, identification, shoulder

Safety points
Take the same precautions as for Activity 1.

General notes
Before pupils attempt this Activity it is important that they are able to identify the plants listed in the quadrat record sheet (page 13 of pupils' book).

Apparatus list
Quadrat
Clip board (preferably covered with clear polythene sheet)
Record sheet
Pen or pencil
Plant identification sheets (from pupils' book)

Details for any construction
See diagram 15, page 90, for construction of a quadrat.

Activity 6:
Line study

Objective
To obtain a rapid indication of changes in vegetation.

Experience
To find out what types of plants are growing in a certain area at 1 m intervals along a 20 m straight line

Skills involved
1. Using and reading a 20 m tape measure
2. Identifying plants using charts
3. Recording observations on the line study record sheet

Unfamiliar words
20 m tape measure, example, names of plants

Safety points
Take the same precautions as for Activity 1.

General notes
To obtain the best results from this Activity it is most important that pupils are familiar with the names of the common plants and that they are able to identify them. Make sure they have the skill to use the 20 m tape and that plants are recorded only at 1 m intervals.

Apparatus list
2 pegs (small tent pegs are best)
20 m tape measure
Pencil
Record sheet
Plant identification sheet (from pupils' book) or plant book

Details for any construction
None

Activity 7:
Belt study

Objective
Study gradual changes in vegetation across an area, and to think about possible reasons for this

Experience
To find which of the 12 plants listed on the record sheet can be found in a certain area using the belt study method

Skills involved
1. Using and reading a 20 m tape measure

2. Placing quadrats at correct distances along the tape
3. Identifying the 12 plants listed on the record sheet
4. Recording observations

Unfamiliar words
Stretch, distance, opposite

Safety points
Take the same precautions as for Activity 1.

General notes
1. Make sure that pupils can identify the 12 plants listed on the record sheet (page 17 of pupils' book).
2. Since this is the third method of sampling that the pupils have carried out, it is important that a class discussion should follow to compare each method and to interpret results.

Apparatus list
Record sheet
Pencil
20 m tape measure
Quadrat frames
2 pegs (tent pegs are useful)
Plant identification sheets (from pupils' book)
Clip board would be useful

Details for any construction
See diagram 15, page 90, for construction of the quadrat frames.

Activity 8:
Uses of plants

Objective
Ability to recognise plants which have been used in the design and planning of local environments in order to satisfy some criteria

Experiences
1. To visit a park to try to recognise some of the plants growing there
2. To decide why those plants were planted there in the first place

Skills involved
1. Using plant identification charts or books as an aid to plant recognition

2. Making a decision and recording the reasons for making that particular decision

Unfamiliar words
Unusual, column

Safety points
Take the same precautions as for Activity 1.

General notes
1. Some pupils may have difficulty in making decisions; help may be needed here.
2. Pupils should be encouraged to attempt some simple design and planning of a local 'landscape'.

Apparatus list
Plant identification book
Tree and shrub book
Record sheet
Pencil
Clip board would be useful

Details for any construction
None

Activity 9:
Industry and wild life

Objective
To encourage pupils to take an interest in their local environment and to suggest ways of improving it

Experiences
1. To visit an area near an industrial site or some derelict land and make observations to find out if there are plants, animals or birds in that area
2. To suggest areas where wild plants, animals and birds might be able to live

Skills involved
1. Ability to make observations
2. Ability to make decisions
3. Ability to use a given code to record ideas for making improvements in the local environment

Unfamiliar words
Acres, derelict, industry, reclamation, government, islands, beaches, disturbed, buildings

Safety points
Take the same precautions as for Activity 1, but see also 'Notes for teacher'.

General notes
This Activity could be used to try to develop an active interest in the need to provide facilities for plant, animal and bird life in local environments.

Apparatus list
Plain paper or some sheets of drawing paper
Pencil
Clip board would be useful

Details for any construction
None

Answers to questions in pupils' book

All the answers in this Unit depend on the locality the school is in and on the areas chosen for investigation, except for the identification of the plants in the photo quiz on the back cover. These are as follows:

1. Rosebay willow-herb
2. Thistle
3. Stinging nettle
4. Shepherd's purse
5. Ribwort plantain

DIAGRAM 15. Construction of a quadrat frame (Activities 5 and 7).

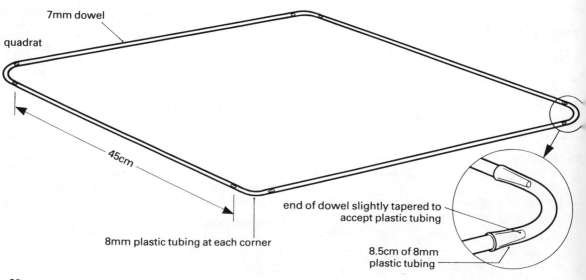

7mm dowel

quadrat

45cm

8mm plastic tubing at each corner

end of dowel slightly tapered to accept plastic tubing

8.5cm of 8mm plastic tubing

DIAGRAM 16. Construction of a Tulgren funnel
(Activity 4).

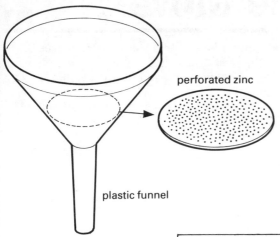

perforated zinc

plastic funnel

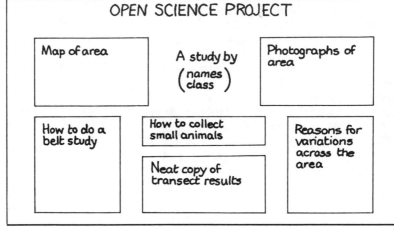

Chart 1.

Chart 2.

Machines on the Move

Summary of contents

Since the majority of machines today are powered by an electric motor or an internal combustion engine this Unit considers both these methods of providing the motive or driving power of these machines.

The structure of the electric motor is considered in some detail, but pupils are encouraged to construct their own model from clear and detailed illustrations. The models are then used to demonstrate some of the principles involved. The importance of not overloading the motor is also considered since damage could result. How to prevent this happening is further demonstrated by using cut-outs.

The second part of the Unit focuses on the car engine. Initially the pupils construct a model car battery which they charge and then discharge by lighting a lamp. The Unit then leads them to consider how the chemical energy from the fuel can be used to produce mechanical energy in the cylinders and how this energy can be transmitted to the driving wheels. The ignition system is discussed and demonstrated in detail, including the structure and function of the contact breaker and distributor.

Finally the pupils are led to consider the wiring of a starter motor, the need for a solenoid switch in the circuit and the need for both thick and thin wires in the circuit.

Equipment list for whole of Unit

To be made
Model railway track (Activity 1)
Electric motor/cut-out board (Activities 3 and 4)
Model car cylinder complete with pistons (Activity 8)

Mounting for coil and solenoid (Activities 8, 10, 11 and 12)
Support stand for distributor (Activities 8, 10 and 11)
Mounting for ignition switch (Activities 10, 11 and 12)
Mounting for sparking plugs (Activity 11)
Starter motor stand with plastic safety cage (Activity 12)

To be bought or obtained from other departments
Small lengths of brass rod
Tinplate sheets (for model electric motor)
Metal rods
Wood for construction of apparatus and models
Lead foil (to be cut into strips)
Blotting paper
Car batteries
Charts of car engine showing four stroke cycle
Filmstrip or slides on the car and car engine (could be hired or borrowed)
Plastic tube/sheet
Spark plugs
Metal rod
Balsawood for piston
Wheel and bearing from meccano
Ignition coil
Contact breaker
Distributor
Spade tags for leads
Ignition lead
Ignition switches
H.T. leads
Solenoid switch
Low voltage orbit motor
Electric cut-out (from R.S. Components Ltd.)
Note: Many of the car accessories could be bought cheaply second hand, e.g. from a scrap car dealer

To be collected
Model railway track
Plastic house guttering (box type)

Assumed normally available in laboratory

Low voltage supply
Magnets
Leads (with 4 mm plugs and croc clips)
Insulating tape
Cotton covered wire (S.W.G. 24 and 26)
Scissors
4½ V dry batteries
Pliers
Wire cutters
Screwdrivers
Screws

Nails
Glass paper
Various types of masses
Ammeter (0-1 A)
Nylon thread
Beakers
Elastic bands
Sulphuric acid (dilute)
Voltmeters (0-5 V)
M.E.S. lampholders
Lamps (3.5 V and 2.5 V)
Stop clock

Forward planner

Activity number	Advanced planning needed	Approximate Activity time (40 min period)	Are results of a previous Activity necessary?
1	None *	1 period	No
2	Cut tinplate strips to size required. Also drill holes in relevant places	4 periods	No
3	None *	1 period	No
4	None *	1 period	No
5	Cut lead foil to size and also blotting paper	1 period	No
6	None	2 periods	Activity 5 (model car battery)
7	Obtain slides, filmstrips, film or charts giving relevant information	1 or 2 periods	No
8	None *	2 periods	No
9	Obtain duplicated diagrams of four stroke cycle	3 periods	Activity 8
10	None *	3 periods	No
11	None *	2 periods	Activity 10
12	None *	3 or 4 periods	No

* Assumes that apparatus for these Activities has already been made.

Notes for teacher

There is a link here with *Find out about Machines* where in Activity 1 pupils were asked to consider the motive power of many different machines.

They should discover that the majority of machines are powered by either an electric motor or an internal combustion engine.

Hopefully at some time during the course of lessons on this topic the teacher might consider with the class whether these types of machines will continue to be the main method of powering machines in the future.

Activity 1
This Activity demonstrates two things: (a) that electricity can be used to make things move, and (b) that the direction of movement

will depend upon (i) the direction of the electric current, and (ii) the direction of the magnetic field.

Activity 2
Since the parts needed to make this model electric motor are easily obtainable and fairly inexpensive it is hoped that each pupil could make his or her own model. The motor should operate using most types of magnet. Pupils who show interest in the motor may be encouraged to redesign it by replacing the magnets with an electromagnet.

Activity 3
The results of this Activity help the pupils to realise that the small electric motors used in the laboratory are d.c. motors. For a class who are particularly interested, a discussion on different types of motors could follow the Activity, but this should not be laboured.

Activity 4
This shows that an increased current is taken by the motor when the load is increased. If the motor is overloaded, the windings inside could burn out. An automatic cut-out can prevent this happening — some lawn mowers are protected in this way.

Activities 5 and 6
The strength of the acid is not particularly critical, but it should not be too dilute.

During electrolysis the solution may get quite warm — warn pupils to take care. Warning should be given about the careful use of acids. Safety goggles should be worn.

Classes will need to be warned about the correct polarity when connecting the voltmeter. With some classes teachers may prefer each group to ask for help before connecting the voltmeter for the first time.

At 6 V d.c. the current will be approximately 5 A. You will need to check that the power supply to be used can supply this current without damage to the power pack.

After the class has had a chance to produce their own model car batteries it is anticipated that the teacher will discuss the work and the answers to the questions with the pupils. Much of the discussion can take place while the groups are working.

Question 4 may lead to the possibility of using larger lead plates in the 'sandwich'.

With a class who are particularly interested this work has potential for development.

Activity 7
An Activity on the car engine and its parts can be arranged around the photograph on page 17 of the pupils' book. This is a good point at which to discuss the car engine generally.

It is hoped, of course, that various forms of visual aids, such as slides, filmstrips, charts or even film can be used to familiarise the pupils with the various parts that form the main components of a car engine.

Activity 8
Each of the two parts of this Activity is a demonstration and the teacher should try each one before attempting to demonstrate it to the class.

It is suggested that the lesson should start immediately with the two demonstrations using the model car cylinder and that this work will be most effective if the apparatus is set up ready before the lesson.

Note: The important point here is what happens in the cylinder, not the circuitry used to produce the spark at the plug.

The first demonstration should be followed immediately by the second, the teacher asking orally the questions to be found in the pupils' book — pupils should then attempt to answer the questions. With an especially slow group the teacher may wish to go through the answers with the class before pupils attempt them.

The circuitry for the first demonstration is shown in diagram 17, page 108. The piston is free to move up the metal rod. The gas supply is turned on for 4 seconds and the contact breaker spindle is turned quickly to produce sparks at the plug. The gas-air mixture explodes and forces the piston up the rod. The piston drops and more gas-air is added to repeat the process.

The function of the bunsen burner is to ensure a gas-air mixture enters the cylinder. (This could be reinforced by discussing how two types of flame can be produced with a lit bunsen burner.)

In a car the carburettor ensures a petrol-air mixture enters the cylinder.

For the second demonstration the second piston replaces the first. In this case the piston is fastened to the piston rod, which is connected at the other end to the counterbalanced wheel.

The first piston is removed by pulling out the metal rod from the wooden stand. The wheel axle is then pushed into the hole in the centre of the bearing. (See diagram 22, page 110.)

On explosion of the mixture, the up and down movement of the wooden piston is changed into the rotary motion of the wheel. The piston needs to be moved up and down a number of times to clear the cylinder of gas before repeating the experiment.

When the class has completed the questions the teacher can discuss with them the arrangement of the cylinders in an actual car engine.

The action of the crankshaft could be shown in a simplified form by bending a length of thick copper wire into the shape below.

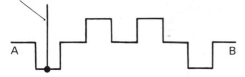

Straight wire represents piston rod of one cylinder

A   B

Demonstration of the action of the crankshaft

The shape can then be rotated between the thumb and forefinger, clearly showing that two pistons rise as the two other pistons are falling in the cylinders.

The advantage of a number of cylinders is that more power is produced and the movement is smoother.

Activity 9

The teacher first discusses the four stroke cycle with the class (a chart showing the four stroke cycle will be useful here).

The combustion of the petrol-air mixture in the cylinder produces heat energy which is converted into mechanical power by the pistons and then into rotary movement by the crankshaft.

Each cylinder goes through four stages to produce its power:

1. *The induction stroke*
   The inlet valve is open and the exhaust valve is closed. As the piston descends the reduced pressure causes the petrol-air mixture to be pushed into the cylinder by atmospheric pressure. Shortly afterwards the inlet valve closes.

2. *The compression stroke*
   Both the valves are closed.
   The piston rises compressing the gas and causing it to become hot. The degree of compression is measured by the compression ratio — the ratio of the volume of gas inside the cylinder before and after compression. Just before the piston reaches the top of the cylinder the compressed mixture is ignited by a spark from the spark plug.

3. *The power stroke*
   The expansion of the gas pushes the piston down and the exhaust valve begins to open as the piston approaches the bottom of the cylinder.
   The mixture burns rapidly across the top of the cylinder. If the compression ratio is too high for the petrol being used (e.g. 2 star petrol in a 1300 engine) then some of the mixture furthest away from the spark plug will explode — this is known as knocking or pinking.
   Pre-ignition can also lead to loss of efficiency and overheating — in this case the petrol self-ignites before the spark occurs. Possible causes of this are (a) defective spark plugs or (b) carbon deposits in the cylinder which glow hot continuously (however, this rarely occurs with modern petrols).

4. *The exhaust stroke*
   The inlet valve is closed and the exhaust valve is open. The rising piston expels the burnt gases from the cylinder. The exhaust valve closes, inlet valve opens and the cycle begins over again.

95

After pupils have completed the Activity some or all of the following points could be discussed, depending on the interest of the class at this stage.

1. Why do we need to use the correct grade of petrol in our car?
2. Why should spark plugs be checked frequently?
3. Pre-ignition — de-coking (i.e. removing deposits of carbon from the cylinders and valves) is not usually necessary nowadays.

It may be more helpful to the pupils if the teacher discusses only two or three questions (page 22 of pupils' book) at one time before attempts are made to answer them.

Coloured charts showing the work of the pistons would help greatly here.

Activity 10

The circuit should be set up in front of the class, the names of the different parts being introduced as they are wired into the circuit.

The circuitry is the same as shown on page 23 of the pupils' book.

The single spark plug should be supported in a clamp stand (e.g. burette stand).

For the second part of the Activity the contact breaker is introduced into the circuit, as shown on page 24 of the pupils' book.

The second part of the Activity should follow on immediately from the first part, the teacher asking orally the questions to be found on pages 24 and 25 of the pupils' book.

The class can then complete the Activity as far as question 3. While the class are doing this, the teacher can ask smaller groups to come, in turn, around the apparatus to show them the inside of the contact breaker and explain the action of the points.

The spindle turns the cam. As it turns, the cam pushes on the heel and causes the points to separate.

As the cam turns further the spring causes the points to come together again, i.e. as the cam turns the contact between the points is continually made and broken (hence the name contact breaker).

For pupils who are particularly interested, this Activity could be extended to include cleaning and setting the points.

1. Start to undo the screw shown on the drawing below.
2. Turn the spindle so that the heel sits on a corner of the cam as shown. (The size of the gap between the points can make a car go faster or slower, and use more or less petrol.)
3. Take the wires off your contact breaker.
4. Clean the points by folding a sheet of fine emery paper back on itself and move it between the points while pressing them together (you may need to turn the cam).

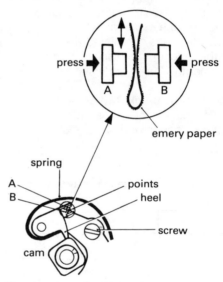

Cleaning the points

In order to set the points to the correct gap you will need a set of feeler gauges. These are sheets of metal with their thickness written on them.

Choose one that is 15 thou. thick (0.015 in. or 15/1000 in.).

1. Set the heel on the corner of the cam and place your feeler gauge between the points.
2. Slide point B across so that it presses on the gauge.
3. Make sure that the heel is still resting on the cam and tighten the screw.

4. Slide the gauge out. The gap should now be as big as the thickness of the feeler gauge.

If the school is able to obtain old contact breakers (e.g. from a scrap yard — pupils will often bring them in if asked) this could be done as a class Activity.

Discussion could also take place about the maintenance of spark plugs.

Activity 11
There are four outlet terminals around the inside of the distributor cap, each of these being connected to a sparking plug. In the centre of the cap is the inlet terminal and current is fed in here from the coil.

The rotor arm fits inside the cap and joins the input terminal to each of the four output terminals, in turn, as it spins.

The rotor arm is placed on top of the contact breaker spindle. The distributor cap is then placed on top of the contact breaker and fastened by the two clips.

A wire is joined from the terminal in the centre of the coil to the middle, input terminal, of the distributor cap. Each of the four outlet terminals are now joined to the plugs as shown in the circuit diagram on page 27 of the pupils' book.

Arrange the leads from the output terminals to the plugs so that the plugs 'fire' in the order 1,3,4,2.

Below are some questions the pupils might be asked.

First, the pupils should be shown the inside of the distributor cap, with four leads connected to the top of the cap.
1. Where do you think these four leads are meant to connect to in the engine?
2. Where does the high voltage electricity enter the distributor?
3. What will happen as the rotor arm spins inside the cap?

Next, wire up the circuit and spin the spindle of the contact breaker.
1. What can we see happening?
2. In what order do the plugs 'fire'?

Discuss the need for replacing the leads in the correct order when working on the engine.

The leads when removed from the plugs should be marked so that they can be replaced in the correct position. This ensures that the cylinders will fire in the correct order (1,3,4,2 or 1,2,4,3).

Activity 12
The function of the starter motor is to turn the engine until it fires and can run under its own power. The turning force required to do this is very large and the motor consequently takes a very high current from the battery. (It can draw as much as 360 A.) This will lead to difficulty in starting if the battery is not fully charged.

Because of the very high current involved, thick leads are needed from the battery to the motor. Also a heavy duty switch — the solenoid — is needed to operate the starter motor.

The solenoid is operated by the ignition switch mounted close to the driver on the dashboard or steering column. The starter motor and solenoid are connected to the battery by thick leads which carry the heavy current needed by the motor. The leads to the ignition are thin as they only need to carry a small current.

Below is suggested one way in which the demonstration can be conducted together with questions that the teacher might ask. The circuit diagrams are shown on pages 29, 30 and 31 of the pupils' book.

The whole of the procedure below (1-8) should be demonstrated to the class and the questions asked orally. The teacher can then go through pages 29-32 of the pupils' book with the class, discussing the answers to the questions and possibly demonstrating each part again as a reinforcement. Some teachers may prefer the pupils to attempt answering the questions one section at a time.

1. Discuss with the class the need for a starter motor (mention could be made of the 'old days' and the hard work involved using a starter handle) and the heavy drain that the starter motor causes on the battery.

2. The starter motor and ignition switch are wired in series with the battery using thin wires. The yellow wires should be used for this. The wires will get hot and the plastic begin to melt. **The starter motor should not be operated for too long.**

Questions asked orally:

What happens to the wires?

What would happen if the motor was kept running?

What sort of wire would not get hot?

3. Wire up the same circuit but use thick wires instead of the thin wires.

Questions:

Do these wires get hot? (No, but it would be expensive.)

Where is (1) the ignition switch in a car?
            (2) the starter motor?

4. Tell the class that there are switches that can be made to work using a small amount of electricity (small current). Wire in series using thin wire, the ignition switch, solenoid and car battery. Operate the ignition switch.

Questions:

What can you hear?

What do you think is happening inside the solenoid? (circuit being made and broken)

Do the wires get hot?

5. With the circuit still as in 4, connect a small dry cell and lamp to the solenoid. When the ignition switch is operated the bulb should light. This is to show the solenoid is in fact a switch, operated by a small current when the ignition switch is closed.

Questions:

What happens to the bulb?

How many switches are we using now?

You (a pupil should be used here) operate one switch — what works the other one?

6. Remove the bulb and dry cell and connect the starter motor instead using thick leads. Operate the motor for a while (turn ignition switch).

Questions:

What happens now?

Do thin wires get hot?

Do the thick wires get hot?

Why do you think solenoids are not mounted behind the dashboard? (thick wires expensive; difficult to bend)

Where do you think they might be mounted? (close to battery and starter motor)

Does the ignition switch have to be close to the rest of the equipment?

7. To demonstrate the last question the short thin wires should be replaced by very long thin wires stretched right across the lab. The ignition switch can then be operated at a distance from the motor, solenoid and battery.

8. Where else could solenoid switches be used?

(e.g. control room operating heavy equipment at a distance.)

Main objectives and ideas

Main objectives

1. To appreciate that an electric current can be used to produce motion
2. Familiarity with the principle of operation of an electric motor
3. Awareness that electic motors can be overloaded but cut-out devices can be included in the circuit to prevent this
4. The structure, function and maintenance of a car battery
5. Knowledge of how the car engine converts chemical energy into mechanical energy
6. An understanding of the main principles of the four stroke cycle
7. Knowledge of the function of the contact breaker and distributor
8. Appreciation of the use of the solenoid switch in relation to the starter motor

Key ideas

1. Awareness that the direction of movement of a conductor depends upon
   (a) the direction of the electric current and
   (b) the direction of the magnetic field
2. To relate parts of a model electric motor to parts of a real motor.
3. To appreciate that the electric current in our homes is a.c. (if d.c. motors are used the current must be rectified)

4. That there is a relationship between the load put on a motor and the amount of current used
5. That cut-outs can be used in motors to prevent damage being caused by overloading
6. That the contents of car batteries are dangerous
7. The important role of the carburettor in supplying the engine with the correct petrol-air mixture
8. Simple maintenance of engine accessories
9. Understanding why thin and thick leads are used in the electric circuitry of a car
10. Understanding why a solenoid switch is needed in the battery — starter motor circuit

Information for each Activity

Activity 1:
Using electricity to make things move

Objective
Awareness that when a d.c. current passes through a conductor a magnetic field is set up

Experience
To show that electrical energy can be converted into mechanical energy with the aid of a magnet

Skills involved
1. To connect up apparatus as shown in a diagram
2. Arranging brass rod and magnet in correct positions
3. Using low voltage power supply
4. Making observations and recording results

Unfamiliar words
Instructions, direction

Safety points
None

General notes
1. The main idea to be developed here is that electricity will produce movement.
2. It is important that the rail is cleaned with emery cloth before starting the experiment.

Apparatus list
Model railway track on a wooden base with push button switch
Small brass rod
Low voltage supply (4 V d.c.)
Magnet (magnadur type)
4 mm plug leads or 4 mm plug and crocodile clip leads

Details for any construction
See diagram 18, page 108 for the mounting for the model railway track.

Activity 2:
Making a model electric motor

Objective
Knowledge of how a simple electric motor works

Experience
Constructing a model electric motor

Skills involved
1. Ability to read and follow detailed instructions with the aid of diagrams
2. Ability to follow a logical sequence of instructions
3. To assemble and check the construction of the model

Unfamiliar words
Tinplate, insulating tape, cotton covered wire, armature, uncovered, squash, baseboard, axle, brushes, position, reverse

Safety points
None

General notes
1. Although this is a simple model it is important that instructions 7, 8 and 11 are carried out correctly, particularly 8 (page 5 of pupils' book).

2. Since this model is cheap to produce the number of pupils per group should be limited to two or three.

Apparatus list

Tinplace cut to the following dimensions:
   2 strips 4 cm × 1½ cm
   2 strips 6 cm × 1½ cm
   2 strips 8 cm × 2   cm with holes 1 cm from each end
Metal rod about 3 mm diameter and about 16 cm long (this can be made from any metal – silver steel, welding rods or steel knitting needles)
Wooden base about 8 cm × 18 cm
Insulating tape
Cotton covered copper wire (24 or 26 S.W.G.)
2 magnets (eclips type)
Scissors
4½ V battery, or low voltage supply (d.c.)
Pliers
Screws
Screwdrivers
Medium or fine glass paper

Details for any construction
None

Activity 3:
A small electric motor (1)

Objective
To understand why a cut-out mechanism is used in an electric circuit as a safety device

Experience
Using a low voltage electric motor to find out how a cut-out mechanism works and why it is used

Skills involved
1. Using and setting up a low voltage unit
2. Connecting up a circuit by making use of diagrams and written instructions
3. Making observations and recording results

Unfamiliar words
Mounted, variable, pulley, terminals, increased, rotation, usually, appliances

Safety points
None

General notes
This Activity is useful in three ways. It shows:
(a) how voltage affects the speed of the motor
(b) how direction of rotation depends on the way in which the motor is wired up
(c) what causes the cut-out to operate

Apparatus list
Electric motor/cut-out board
Copper wire (bare) about 24 S.W.G.
Low voltage a.c. supply (2 V)
Variable d.c. supply (2-4 V)

Details for any construction
See diagram 19, page 109 for construction of the electric motor/cut-out board

Activity 4:
A small electric motor (2)

Objective
To appreciate the reason why cut-outs are used in many domestic appliances

Experience
Finding the relationship between the load lifted by the motor and the current used when the cut-out is activated

Skills involved
1. Using and reading an ammeter
2. Threading load to pulley
3. Wiring the circuit according to written instructions and checking with the aid of a diagram
4. Observing, recording and interpreting results

Unfamiliar words
Ammeter, thread, machine

Safety points
1. Care is needed when a small load is lifted since the cut-out does not operate and the load may swing round the pulley.
2. Safety goggles should be worn if using the model shown on page 10 of the pupils'

book. A new and safer design for the baseboard is given in diagram 19, page 109

General notes
1. Some pupils will need help here with the wiring, and with the reading of the ammeter dial.
2. Stress the importance of using low voltages, i.e. 3 V d.c.
3. Pupils may need to be told how to re-set the cut-out.

Apparatus list
Electric motor/cut-out board
Low voltage supply unit (3 V d.c.)
Various masses to be used as loads
Ammeter (0-1 A)
Thread
Scissors
Leads, 4 mm — 4 mm (three)

Details for any construction
See diagram 19, page 109 for construction of electric motor/cut-out board.

Activity 5:
Making a model car battery

Objective
Familiarity with the structure of a car battery

Experience
Making a simple lead-acid model car battery

Skills involved
1. Measuring and cutting lead sheet according to given instructions
2. Assembling the model car battery according to written and illustrated instructions

Unfamiliar words
Lead foil, dilute, sulphuric acid, 'sandwich', touching, blotting paper

Safety points
1. Ensure that pupils wash their hands thoroughly after handling lead sheet.
2. Care must be taken with sulphuric acid.

General notes
1. Since it is important that the blotting paper insulates the individual lead strips it may be important also to stress this by showing an actual demonstration of the technique involved.
2. It may be wise to check the 'plates' assembled by each group before they add the acid.

Apparatus list
Lead foil cut to the following dimensions:
   2 sheets 8 cm × 4 cm
   2 sheets 40 cm × 4 cm
Blotting paper (2 sheets, 45 cm × 5 cm)
Beaker (100 cm³)
Elastic bands
Dilute sulphuric acid

Details for any construction
None

Activity 6:
Using the model car battery

Objective
Awareness that electricity can be stored

Experience
Charging the model car battery and using it to light a lamp

Skills involved
1. Connecting the model battery to the correct terminals of the low voltage supply unit
2. Using a stop watch or stop clock
3. Timing charging and discharging
4. Observing, recording and interpreting results

Unfamiliar words
Voltmeter, battery, terminal, voltage, disconnect, recharge, reconnect

Safety points
Make sure that the beaker is stable — the leads may pull it over.

General notes

1. It may be worthwhile discussing differences between this type of battery and the 'dry battery' used in torches.
2. The Activity could be developed further by reference to a car battery and its maintenance.

Apparatus list

Model car battery
Low voltage power supply (4-6 V d.c.)
2 leads (4 mm plug — croc)
Voltmeter (0-5 V)
2.5 V lamp in holder, preferably mounted on a wooden base, complete with leads and croc clips
Stop clock

Details for any construction
The model car battery is made in Activity 5.

Activity 7:
The motor car engine

Objective

Ability to recognise the 'visible' parts of a motor car engine

Experience

To use charts, filmstrips or various illustrations in order to become familiar with the parts of a car engine

Skills involved

To recognise the names and the parts of a car engine

Unfamiliar words

Cylinders, pistons, flywheel, valves, crankshaft, gears, filters, etc.

Safety points

None

General notes

Although the illustration on page 17 of the pupils' book is very clear and allows an opportunity to name several parts of the engine, this should be complemented with filmstrips, slides or film. If possible take pupils to see a real car engine.

Apparatus list

Charts, filmstrips or slides showing a car engine

Details for any construction
None

Activity 8:
What happens when energy comes from fuel?

Objective

Awareness of how the engine power is produced

Experience

To observe the results of an explosion in a model car cylinder using a gas-air mixture

Skills involved

Ability to observe and record what is seen

Unfamiliar words

Cylinder, energy, increasing volume, movement, rotary

Safety points

If all the instructions are carried out properly and the apparatus is in good working order (see 'Details for any construction') there is no danger; however, it may be wise to use a safety screen.

General notes

1. It is important that pupils are able to relate the names of the parts in the model to the parts in a real engine.
2. It is also important that pupils realise that the energy is provided by a gas-air mixture not a petrol-air mixture. The reason should be given.

Apparatus list

Model car cylinder with 2 piston rods
Bunsen burner
Ignition coil on wooden mount
Distributor with handle on wooden mount
Car battery

Leads:
  4 mm plug — croc. clip
  4 mm plug — spade tag
  spade tag — spade tag
  spade tag — croc. clip
  ignition lead (from coil to spark plug)

Details for any construction
See diagrams 21 and 22, page 111 for construction of the model car cylinder and piston rods. Suitable mountings for the ignition coil and distributor are shown in diagram 20, page 109 and diagram 23, page 111.
  A wiring diagram is given on page 108 (diagram 17).
  The distributor needs to be turned fairly fast. It is therefore essential to fit a turning handle to the centre spindle of the distributor.

Activity 9:
The four stroke cycle

Objective
To understand the four stroke cycle in the car engine

Experience
Cutting and pasting in the spaces provided the following pictures: inlet stroke, compression stroke, power stroke, exhaust stroke

Skills involved
Ability to place illustrations in the correct sequence to represent the four stroke cycle

Unfamiliar words
Cycle, movements, piston, compression, exhaust, diagrams, information, opposite, expands

Safety points
None

General notes
Obviously the use of some kind of visual aid would be useful here. See 'Notes for teacher' for more details and further suggestions for development.

Apparatus list
Duplicated sheets showing the four strokes:

inlet, compression, power and exhaust (diagrams should show the position of the piston in the cylinder and whether the valves are open or closed; sizes of the cut-outs are critical since they have to fit the rectangles on page 21 of the pupils' book)
Some copper wire, about 20 S.W.G., and pliers are useful for a demonstration of the crankshaft (see 'Notes for teacher')

Details for any construction
None

Activity 10:
The contact breaker

Objective
To understand the function of various parts of a car — the contact breaker

Experiences
1. To find out what a contact breaker is and where it is found
2. To wire up a circuit (diagram provided) including a contact breaker

Skills involved
1. Ability to identify and name the parts to be used
2. Ability to select the correct leads to connect to the various parts of the circuit

Unfamiliar words
Ignition switch, spindle, contact breaker, replacing, adjusting

Safety points
None

General notes
None

Apparatus list
Car battery
Ignition switch (mounted)
Spark plug (supported in clamp stand or burette stand)
Ignition coil on wooden mount
Contact breaker (distributor) on wooden mount

Set of leads:

4 mm plug — spade tag	} red wire
spade tag — spade tag	
spade tag — spade tag	
4 mm plug — spade tag	} black wire
4 mm plug — croc clip	
croc clip — spade tag	green wire

H.T. lead (from coil to spark plug)

Details for any construction
See diagram 20, page 109 and diagram 23, page 111, for construction of the mountings for the coil and distributor. The exact dimensions of the mounts will depend on the makes and sizes of the parts chosen.

The ignition switch should be mounted on a piece of box type plastic house guttering about 14 cm long and 10 cm diameter. Two lengths of braided battery cable are needed at the back, from the terminals of the switch; they should have proper car battery connectors on their free ends.

Activity 11:
The distributor

Objective
To understand the function of various parts of a car — the distributor

Experience
Using a distributor to show how the electricity is sent to each spark plug in turn

Skills involved
1. Identifying each part to be used in the circuit
2. Wiring up the circuit, according to a given diagram
3. Selecting and connecting the appropriate leads

Unfamiliar words
Distributor, electricity, rotor arm, spindle, checked

Safety points
1. The ignition switch should not be left on for long periods since the coil will overheat.
2. Switch off when not being used.

General notes
1. There are many interesting points to be discussed with pupils in this Activity.
2. Check polarity of lead connections before switching on.
3. See 'Notes for teacher' for more detailed instructions.

Apparatus list
Car battery
Ignition switch (mounted)
Ignition coil on wooden mount
Contact breaker and distributor cap on wooden mount
4 spark plugs (mounted)
Set of leads:

4 mm plug — spade tag	} red wire
spade tag — spade tag	
4 mm plug — croc. clip	} black wire
spade tag — spade tag	
spade tag — spade tag	green wire

H.T. leads:
4 from distributor to spark plugs
1 from distributor to coil

Details for any construction
See diagram 20, page 109, diagrams 23 and 24, page 111, for the construction of the mountings for the ignition coil, distributor, and spark plugs. See 'Details for any construction' Activity 10, for the ignition switch mounting.

Activity 12:
Wiring up a starter motor

Objective
To understand the functions of various parts of a car — the starter motor and solenoid switch

Experience
1. Wiring up a starter motor with only the car battery and ignition switch
2. Removing starter motor and replacing it with M.E.S. bulb and 3 V battery connected to solenoid switch
3. Wiring up starter motor with ignition switch, solenoid switch and car battery

Skills involved

1. Identifying the parts to be used
2. Understanding what each part is going to be used for
3. Identifying the leads for each part
4. Following stage by stage instructions
5. Re-checking the wired circuit with the aid of diagrams

Unfamiliar words

Starter motor, solenoid, stretching, dashboard

Safety points

1. It is important that the starter motor is in a secure position and that the shaft is protected with a plastic box (see 'Details for any construction').
2. Care must be taken with 'Thin or thick wires' (What to do: 1). This part of the Activity must be supervised or carried out as a demonstration.

General notes

1. Since this is a lengthy Activity it will need generous discussion time.
2. It is important that each stage is carefully explained and help and guidance given with the questions. See 'Notes for teacher' for more detailed accounts and background.

Apparatus list

Starter motor with safety cage
Car battery
Ignition switch (mounted)
Solenoid on wooden mount
3 V or 4.5 V battery
3 V or 4.5 V lamp and holder (M.E.S. type; use any normal touch bulb and battery)
Set of leads:
  croc clip — croc clip (three)
  4 mm plug — bare end ⎫
  bare end — bare end ⎬ thin wire (yellow)
  bare end — 4 mm plug ⎭
  ring — ring ⎫
  ring/bolt — ring ⎬ thick wire (for battery leads)
  ring/bolt — ring ⎭
  4 mm plug — spade tag ⎫ red wire
  spade tag — spade tag ⎭
  4 mm plug — spade tag   black wire
  4 mm plug — spade tag ⎫ blue wire; the first
  spade tag — spade tag ⎬ two wires must be
  4 mm plug — spade tag ⎭ several metres long

Details for any construction
See diagrams 23 and 25, page 111, for construction of the mounting for the solenoid switch and of the support for the car starter motor, complete with safety cage. See 'Details for any construction', Activity 10, for the ignition switch mounting.

Answers to questions in pupils' book

A letter D indicates that the answer cannot be predicted, usually because it is dependent on the results of the class experiments.

Activity 1
1. No
2. The direction of the current or the direction of the magnetic field (which way round the magnet is)

Activity 2
1. 1) The direction the current flows through the armature
   2) Which way round the magnets are, that is, the direction of the magnetic field

Activity 3
What to do
4. It spins faster. The wires of the armature inside the motor would get red hot (burn out).
7. It does not work. The pulley (armature) only vibrates.
Questions
1. Reverse the flow of current or reverse the voltage of the supply.
2. Any reasonable answer, e.g. to allow a motor (e.g. in a milk float) to give forward or reverse motion, or to allow a load to be lifted and lowered
3. d.c.
4. Because the mains supply is a.c. Note: we can use some appliances on d.c. if we convert the a.c. supply to d.c. first (i.e. rectify it).
5. Fridge, hair dryer, fan heater, vacuum cleaner

Activity 4
1. The current increases. The greater the load, the greater the current taken. (The motor working harder uses more electrical energy.)
2. It increased much more to full scale deflection.
3. The electric cut-out operates, switching off the supply.
4. An electric lawn mower

5. When the machine is working too hard, that is, cutting grass that is long or wet
6. So that if the machine is overloaded the very high current does not burn out the windings of the armature.

Activity 6
1. Bubbles of gas, showing a chemical change is taking place
2. It can be recharged. It can give a bigger current. It has a lower internal resistance.
3. It is able to light the bulb for a longer time.
4. Use bigger lead plates. Recharge for a longer period of time.
5. Real battery is bigger. It gives a bigger voltage (because it is really a number of lead-acid cells connected in series).

Activity 8
Questions: page 18
1. 1) Gas
   2) Air
2. The bunsen burner allows air to be mixed with the gas entering the model cylinder.
3. There is a petrol-air mixture in the cylinder of a car.
4. The carburettor mixes air with petrol vapour.
5. It explodes
6. It makes the volume of the gas expand.
7. It forces it up.
Questions: page 19
1. The wooden piston moves up and the wheel turns.
2. up, down, rotary

Activity 9
What to do
The correct order of diagrams for the four stroke cycle is shown here

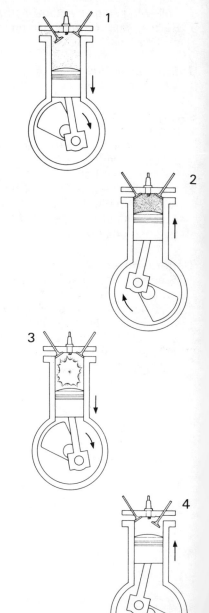

Diagrams of the four stroke cycle.

Questions
1. Four
2. Petrol-air mixture explodes — strictly, fast burns.
3. As each piston moves down it rotates the crankshaft. The crankshaft pushes other pistons back to the top of the cylinder.
4. 1) To give more power
   2) To give smoother running
5. To convert the up and down motion of the pistons into rotary motion
6. The clutch allows the turning crankshaft to be engaged and disengaged with the gears.
7. A large heavy metal wheel that stores kinetic energy
8. It is continually storing and releasing kinetic energy so that a smoother rotation of the crankshaft is obtained, and/or it maintains the rotation of the crankshaft between power strokes.

Activity 10
Questions: page 24
1. The plug sparks.
2. Keep turning the ignition switch on and off.
3. No. Not convenient — could not switch it fast enough.
4. The coil gets hot.
Questions: page 25
1. The plug keeps sparking.
2. To switch on and off rapidly
3. A spark can be seen at the points.

4. The heel
5. The heel opens and closes the points or the points open and close continuously.
6. It recloses the points when the heel has passed over the cam.
7. The points

Activity 11
1. To a plug by an ignition lead
2. Into the central terminal
3. It comes from the coil. It delivers the current in turn to each of the plugs, or it shares out the electricity between the plugs.
4. The plugs each sparked in turn.
5. D. In a car it is usually 1 3 4 2 or 1 2 4 3.
6. Yes; To give reasonably even turning of the crankshaft, or to make the crankshaft rotate smoothly
7. To make sure that they can reconnect them in the correct order
8. 1) To check gap is correct
   2) To check the ceramic insulator is not cracked
   3) To check electrodes for erosion
      To check electrodes for deposits
      To clean plugs

Activity 12
Questions: page 30
1. The starter motor turned.
2. The thin wires got hot. The plastic began to melt.

3. They might burst into flames.
4. Yes. They did not get hot. They can carry a bigger current safely.
5. Towards the bottom of the engine compartment
6. On dashboard inside the car
7. 1) The thick wires are too expensive.
   2) They are difficult to bend around other parts and they take up more space.
Questions: page 31
1. 1) It lights.
   2) It clicks.
2. Two — an ignition switch and a solenoid switch
3. The solenoid
4. No. The circuit with the bulb in is carrying a small current.
Questions: page 32
1. The starter motor turns.
2. No
3. No
4. It is too far to run thick wires from the starter motor to the solenoid.
5. In the engine compartment as close to the starter motor as possible
6. No; Because it can be connected by thin wires
7. Any sensible answer, e.g. remote control of switching from a long distance when convenience or safety demand it

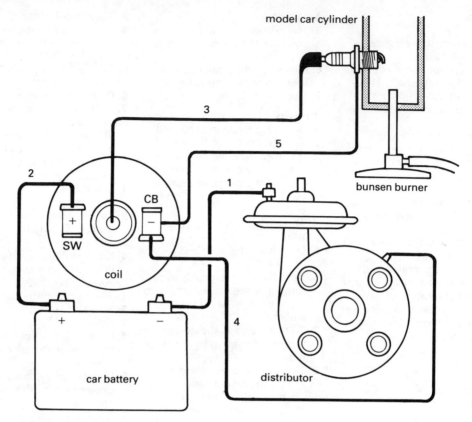

Wires: 1 4mm plug– crocodile clip
        2 4mm plug– spade tag
        3 Ignition lead (to spark plug)
        4 Spade tag– spade tag
        5 Spade tag– crocodile clip

DIAGRAM 17. Wiring diagram for model car cylinder (Activity 8)

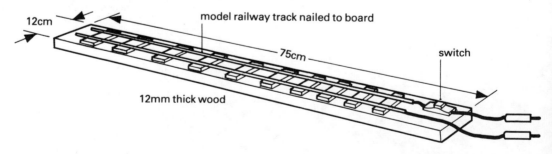

DIAGRAM 18. Construction of mounting for model railway track (Activity 1).

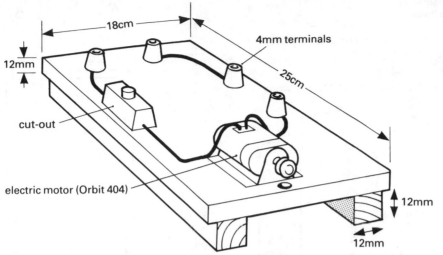

18cm

12mm

4mm terminals

25cm

cut-out

electric motor (Orbit 404)

12mm

12mm

Note: This is an amended version of the apparatus shown in early editions of the pupil's book. Threading the pulley wire through the base board prevents light loads flying into the air.

DIAGRAM 19. Construction of electric motor/cut-out board (Activities 3 and 4).

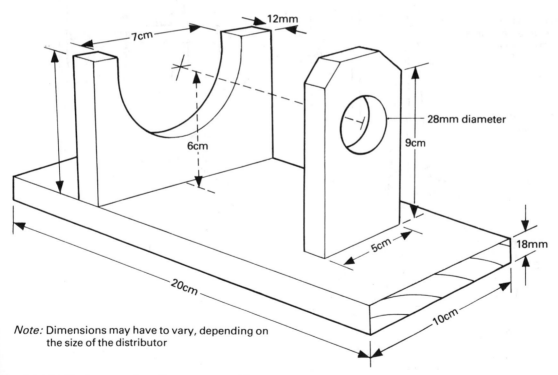

12mm

7cm

28mm diameter

9cm

6cm

5cm

18mm

20cm

10cm

Note: Dimensions may have to vary, depending on the size of the distributor

DIAGRAM 20. Construction of support stand for distributor (Activities 8, 10 and 11).

wheel (75mm diameter),
collars, nuts and bolts –
meccano

balancing weight on wheel - sheet lead
Meccano spindle

small block of wood
7cm

aluminium tube
(4mm internal diameter)

3mm hole (to accept rod 'A')
78cm from base

wooden framework
(preferably 12.5mm hard wood)

perspex cylinder (16cm long,
66mm internal diameter,
76mm external diameter)

85cm

hole for spark plug
½" (12.5mm)

hole for
bunsen burner

sheet perspex

10cm

9.5cm

12cm

20cm

10cm

25cm

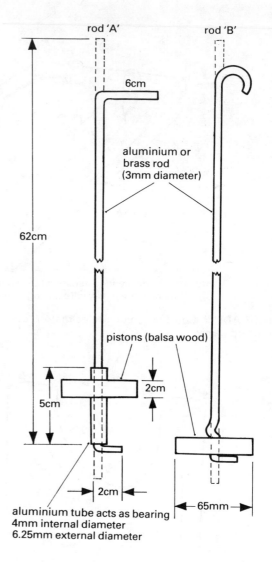

rod 'A'   rod 'B'

6cm

aluminium or
brass rod
(3mm diameter)

62cm

pistons (balsa wood)

2cm

5cm

2cm

aluminium tube acts as bearing
4mm internal diameter
6.25mm external diameter

65mm

DIAGRAM 22. Construction of model piston rods
for model car cylinder (Activity 8).

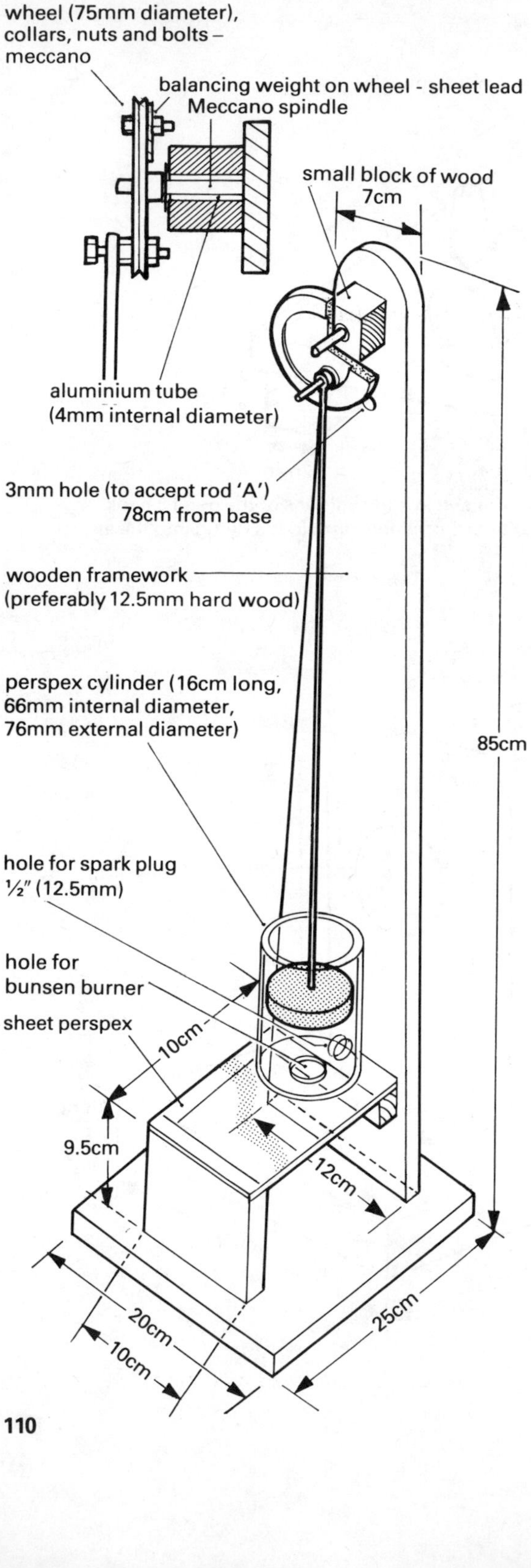

DIAGRAM 21. Construction of model car cylinder
(Activity 8).

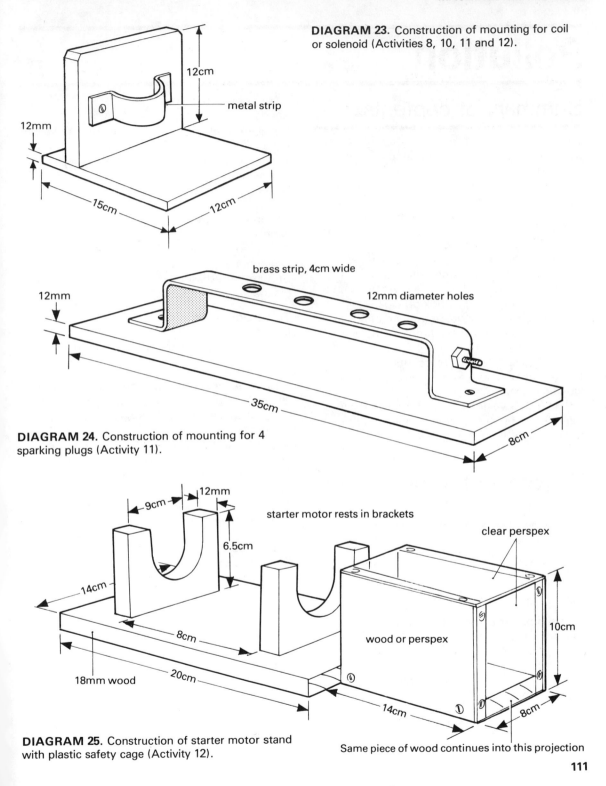

DIAGRAM 23. Construction of mounting for coil or solenoid (Activities 8, 10, 11 and 12).

12cm

metal strip

12mm

15cm

12cm

brass strip, 4cm wide

12mm diameter holes

12mm

35cm

8cm

DIAGRAM 24. Construction of mounting for 4 sparking plugs (Activity 11).

9cm

12mm

starter motor rests in brackets

clear perspex

6.5cm

14cm

8cm

wood or perspex

10cm

18mm wood

20cm

14cm

8cm

DIAGRAM 25. Construction of starter motor stand with plastic safety cage (Activity 12).

Same piece of wood continues into this projection

111

Pollution

Summary of contents

The Unit is designed to show some of the ways in which air, water and land are polluted.

It begins by examining the pollution of the atmosphere by carbon monoxide and sulphur dioxide. (Tests for lead pollution are not included in these experiments because of the lack of suitable apparatus.)

These experiments are followed by investigations on the amounts of solid deposits left on windows in a given time and left in the lungs when smoking cigarettes.

Noise levels in school and in streets nearby are measured at different times of the day using a noise meter.

The Activities on water pollution examine the effects of acidity or otherwise on animal life in the water.

The final investigation on litter collection is intended to open the eyes of pupils to the untidiness of people in general.

Equipment list for whole of Unit

To be made
Wire supports (Activity 3)
Cardboard frames (Activity 5)
Scrapers (Activity 5)
Clip boards (Activities 7, 8, 10, 11)

To be bought or obtained from other departments
Multigas detector kit (Draeger), or 100 cm³ syringe
Draeger tubes for testing for carbon monoxide and carbon dioxide
Large plastic bags (dustbin liners)
Clear plastic bags about 50 × 20 cm
Campden tablets
Seed trays

Seed composts
Seeds
Small amounts of crushed coal and smokeless fuels
Tracing paper or other translucent paper
Cigarettes
Noise meter
Cameras
Waterproof pen
Labels
Animal identification pictures (see 'Notes for teacher')
Growmore fertiliser
Plastic spoons

To be collected
Blood
Exhaust fumes from a car in a large plastic bag (carbon monoxide supply)

Assumed normally available in laboratory
Oxygen cylinder
5 cm³ disposable syringe
Flat bottomed flasks
Beakers and jars
Citric acid solution
Specimen tubes
String
Metal spatulas
Glass tubing
Rubber bungs
Retort stands, clamps and bosses
Bunsen burners
Supply of ice
Bulldog clips
Sheets of plain paper
Compass
Components for smoking machine apparatus
Glass wool
Filter pumps

Universal and comparator indicator papers
Screw top bottles
Rulers
Pond dipping nets
Plastic bowls
Hand lenses
Teat pipettes
Filter funnels
Filter papers
Tripods
Measuring cylinders
Nutrient agar
Petri dishes (glass, pyrex or disposable)
Disposable plastic gloves
Spring balances

Forward planner

Activity number	Advanced planning needed	Approximate Activity time (40 min period)	Are results of a previous Activity necessary?
1	Arrange with the local hospital's blood bank to collect a supply of out of date blood for the day you need it. Alternatively obtain a supply of blood which has been treated so as not to clot from the local abbatoir	2 periods	No
2	Obtain permission from members of teaching staff to collect a sample of the exhaust gases from their cars	2 periods	No
3	Sow seeds in trays 7-14 days before needed. The exact time depends on the season, the greenhouse facilities available and the kinds of seeds used. (Cress and mustard seedlings are well up after about 4 days.) Make wire supports	1 period + 1 period for examination of results and discussion	No
4	Make certain that crushed coal and smokeless fuels are ready for use	2 periods	No
5	Clean windows to be tested about 48 hours beforehand. Make cardboard frames. Make scrapers	1 period for setting up + 1 period for scraping windows and discussing results	No
6	None	1 period	No
7	Make clip boards	1 period	No
8	None	1 period	No
9	These are out of school Activities. Reconnoitre area beforehand	1 period for discussion + 2 periods	No
10			No
11			No
12	Keep the water collected from the river in Activity 9	1 period	Samples from Activity 9
13		1 period	
14	Retain filter papers from Activity 13	1 period + 1 period for discussion of results	Filter papers from Activity 13
15	Ensure that a good supply of seeds, fertiliser and compost is available	1 period for setting up + 1 period for examination of results and discussion	No
16	Discuss beforehand suitable streets for litter collection	2 periods	No

Notes for teacher

Activity 1

The supply of carbon monoxide can be obtained from the exhaust gases from a car, as in Activity 2. (This is the best quick source of the gas since town gas is no longer used.) The supply of oxygen can be from an oxygen cylinder if one is present in the school or from the usual chemical preparation of the gas. Both gases should be collected in fairly large plastic bags and the bags sealed and labelled. These should then be connected up as in diagram 26, page 126, and the gases bubbled very slowly through the blood sample.

The rate of bubbling is controlled by the speed at which the water flows through the filter pump. Slow bubbling is essential to prevent the blood frothing. At the end of the time taken to bubble the gases through, a little of the blood samples including the untreated blood should be poured into flat containers. This makes the detection of any colour changes in the blood easier, especially if the containers are held against a white background.

The containers can be made by placing a length of narrow rubber tubing e.g. bicycle valve tubing, shaped like a letter U between 2 glass plates (microscope slides) held together by elastic bands (see diagram 27, page 126). The blood can be injected into each container using a disposable syringe or teat pipette.

Activity 2

Before starting the car attach a large plastic bag, such as a dustbin liner, firmly to the exhaust pipe with a strong elastic band or string. When the bag is full remove it and close the open end. If an elastic band is used it will do this when the bag is removed. Before testing for the amount of carbon monoxide read carefully the instructions, given with every set of tubes. From these the amount of carbon monoxide in each bag can be determined.
Note: question 1 could be altered to read.... 'Which car gave off the most carbon monoxide? Suggest reasons why'. Then the age, make, servicing, etc. of the car could be

discussed and also the grade of petrol used (2, 3, 4 or 5 star).

As a further, *optional experiment,* tests for the amounts of carbon dioxide inside the car could be carried out immediately before and immediately after passengers sat in and got out of the car. This particular experiment was carried out in one of the schools with very good results. The same detector tube was used throughout the experiment. The pupils sat in the completely closed car for about 5 min.

Activity 3

Ensure that there is a healthy crop of seedlings in each tray. (Cress or mustard seeds are among the best ones to use for this experiment since they germinate quickly.) The wire supports can be placed at each end of the tray if you wish for their only function is to increase the height of the plastic bag so increasing the amount of air inside. The approximate size of the seed trays used in the trials was 370 mm × 240 mm and the clear plastic bags 500 mm × 300 mm.

Sow approximately 50 seeds per tray. It will be difficult to count the numbers of seedlings if you sow more.

Activity 4

This Activity is more or less self explanatory. Use a plastic bag about 300 mm × 200mm for collecting the gases. The bag can be held in place with a strong elastic band.

Activity 5

Clean the windows to be tested about 48 hours beforehand. Once the window is cleaned pupils can fix a frame on the inside of the window. When a scrape is made ensure that the scraper is kept within the area to be tested.

Greaseproof paper could be used instead of tracing paper for measuring the deposit.

The concentration of deposits and hence pollution could be determined as follows:

None	— no line on the paper
Slight	— line on the paper disappears after being covered with 1 or 2 sheets of paper

Medium — line disappears after covering with 3 or 4 sheets of paper

Heavy — line disappears after covering with 5 or 6 sheets of paper

Very heavy — line disappears only after covering with 7 or more sheets

Activity 6

Make sure the apparatus for the smoking machine is available. Pupils may need help with the construction.

Activities 7 and 8

The noise meter must be kept at the same distance from all sources of sound if the results are to be meaningful.

Discuss beforehand where these Activities should be carried out and where practicable the times of the day when they should be done.

The following is a suggested code for sound levels:

Very quiet (A) — below 30 decibels
Quiet (B) — 30-50 decibels
Satisfactory (C) — 50-80 decibels
Loud (D) — 80-90 decibels
Very loud (E) — 90-100 decibels
Dangerously loud (F) — 100 + decibels

WATER POLLUTION

When exploring rivers, streams and canals the following precautions *must* be taken:

1. Check the depth of the water.
2. Impress upon pupils the dangers of deep water especially where the rivers etc. are unfenced.
3. Stress the dangers of walking along untested banks.
4. Ensure that there is no fooling about especially near the water's edge.
5. Make certain that pupils bring suitable clothing for these Activities, e.g. gumboots or wellingtons, waterproof anoraks, etc.
6. Always carry with you the following:
   A first aid kit
   A bottle of antiseptic, e.g. Savlon
   Tablets of soap
   Paper towels
   Plastic bowls or buckets
7. Emphasise the importance of hygiene when working with water and mud. Make certain that all students wash their hands thoroughly after doing their fieldwork.

Activity 9

Collect the water samples at the same depth from each place on the river. See that the tops are screwed firmly back on to the bottles when the water has been collected.

Activity 10

A plankton net may be better for this Activity. It is similar to an ordinary pond dipping net except that it has a hole at its base into which fits a specimen tube (a glass tube about 7.5 cm long and 2.5 cm in diameter). This is secured in position with an elastic band or string.
Note: under the heading 'You need' in the pupils' book, 'nets' should read 'pond dipping nets and handles'. The Biology department should be able to supply these.

Activity 11

The wooden scrapers may be any flat pieces of wood. They are used to push the mud to one side as the pupils look for living things in the mud.

Suitable animal identification pictures may be found in the Philip Harris Study Packs (see 'Relevant information', page 116,).

Activity 12

This Activity is self explanatory and needs no further information.

Activity 13

Shake up the bottles of water well before filtering.

The filtrate (filtered water) from this Activity can be retained and used for the following additional Activity. Transfer 3-4 cm³ of the filtrate on to a microscope slide. Heat this over a low heat until all the water has evaporated. Compare the deposits left on the slides from the different parts of the river.

Activity 14

Under no circumstances must the petri dishes be opened when they are being examined. Viewing from the top or bottom side will give the necessary answers. After use either autoclave the dishes intact at 120°C or place them in an incinerator.

Activity 15

Mix the fertiliser thoroughly with a handful of sand before sprinkling it over the sand. This will ensure a more even spread of fertiliser. Watering is best done using a spray which produces a fine mist either by pressure or by hand operation. A rose from a watering can will *not* produce a fine enough spray and the seeds will be displaced.

When carrying out instruction 13 try not to get any fertiliser on the leaves of the seedlings for they will suffer damage known as 'scorching'.

Activity 16

Discuss with the class the areas which are best suited for this Activity.

Suggested headings for the record (tally) sheets: newspapers, plastic bags, tins, bottles, cigarette packets, matchboxes, etc.

Main objectives and ideas

Main objectives

1. To develop an awareness that excess gases, solids and noise can have harmful effects upon ourselves, other animals and on plants especially those of economic value
2. To develop an awareness that pollution of our streams, rivers, etc. with industrial waste and other effluents can severely affect life therein
3. To develop skills in testing for gases and measuring noise levels
4. To train pupils to observe carefully and record their observations accurately
5. To develop an appreciation of the need to look after the environment by being 'pollution conscious'

Key ideas

1. That some gases are always dangerous to health no matter how small the amount, and that others are only harmful in large amounts, e.g. sulphur dioxide
2. That excessive amounts of solid particles when breathed in can have harmful effects on the lungs, e.g. silicosis

3. That effluents and heat waste can seriously affect life in nearby streams, rivers, etc.
4. That the dropping of litter in streets can lead to infestations of rats and other vermin

Relevant information

Films
1. 'Air Pollution' (3 films), Centre for Extension Studies, Loughborough University of Technology, Loughborough, Leicestershire LE11 3TU
2. 'Pollution of Broccoli and Pelicans, Celery and Seals', Gateway Films Ltd, 29-31 Broad Street, Bristol BS1 2HF

Slides, pictures and study packs
1. 'Air Pollution', Educational Productions Ltd, Bradford Road, East Ardsley, Wakefield WF3 2JN (produced in collaboration with the Gas Council)
2. 'Extraction, Conservation and Pollution', Aerofilms Ltd, 4 Albemarle Street, London W1X 4HR
3. 'Pollution', Folios 1, 2 and 3, The Rickett Encyclopedia of Slides, Portman House, 14 Brodrick Road, London SW17
4. Pollution Study Packs. Set PP1 'Air Pollution'; set PP2 'Stream and River Pollution' from Philip Harris Biological Ltd, Oldmixon, Weston-super-Mare, Avon BS24 9BJ.

Pamphlets and books
1. Various pamphlets and books are available from the National Society for Clean Air, 134-137 North Street, Brighton BN1 1RG
2. 'People and Resources' Series, published by Evans Brothers Ltd, London
3. 'The Unclean Planet' by R.E. Baker and J.A. Bushell, Ginn and Co Ltd, London

Gas detector kit
Details from Draeger Safety Ltd, Draeger House, Sunnyside Rd, Chesham, Bucks. (telephone 02405 74481).

The kit costs £47.30 (1979 prices) and packs of 10 tubes are £6-£7. It is possible and cheaper to buy the pump (£36.85) alone than the kit.

Trial schools used tubes CH 25601 (carbon monoxide 5-700 p.p.m.) and CH 31701 (sulphur dioxide 1-20 p.p.m.) but schools are advised initially to buy the following two tubes which have a wider range:

Carbon monoxide 10/b CH 20601 (carbon monoxide 10-3000 p.p.m.)

Sulphur dioxide 20/a CH 24201 (sulphur dioxide 20-2000 p.p.m.).

Information for each Activity

Apparatus list
Blood in small jar (see 'Forward planner')
Supply of oxygen
Supply of carbon monoxide (see 'Notes for teacher')
Flask labelled 'with oxygen'
Flask labelled 'with carbon monoxide'
5 cm³ disposable syringe

Details for any construction
None

Activity 1:
Carbon monoxide poisons blood

Objective
Awareness that carbon monoxide gas is poisonous and dangerous to health

Experience
To see what happens when carbon monoxide is bubbled through blood

Skills involved
1. Measuring volume using plastic syringes
2. Carrying out a set of detailed instructions
3. Observing and recording of results

Unfamiliar words
Oxygen, carbon monoxide, disposable, syringe, labelled, poison

Safety points
1. Good ventilation is important in the laboratory.
2. Care must be taken when collecting carbon monoxide from exhaust of car.
3. Pupils must be warned not to deliberately inhale the gas used for this Activity.

General notes
. See 'Forward planner' re blood supply.
. See 'Notes for teacher' for method of obtaining carbon monoxide.
. It may be wise to explain some of the differences between carbon monoxide and carbon dioxide.

Activity 2:
Carbon monoxide from car exhausts

Objective
Awareness that carbon monoxide gas is present in car exhaust fumes

Experience
To measure and compare the amount of carbon monoxide in exhaust gases from cars of different ages

Skills involved
1. Method of collecting gas in plastic bag
2. Connecting Draeger tube to plastic bag in such a way as to avoid leaks
3. Using Draeger pump
4. Reading Draeger tubes re colour change
5. Recording results in table provided

Unfamiliar words
Multigas detector kit, Draeger tubes, pump, squeeze

Safety points
1. See 'Safety points' for Activity 1.
2. See 'Notes for teacher' for suggestions on collecting the gas. A teacher must be present when gases are collected.
3. Avoid breathing gas from collector bag.

General notes
1. Careful note taking is important.
2. Care must be exercised when transporting the bag filled with exhaust fumes to the laboratory.

117

3. A general discussion on why older cars need proper servicing might be appropriate.

Apparatus list
Multigas detector kit
Special Draeger tubes for measuring carbon monoxide
4 plastic bags (large)
A selection of different aged cars (need teachers' permission)

Details for any construction
None

Activity 3:
Sulphur dioxide and plants

Objective
Knowledge that sulphur dioxide gas is an air pollutant

Experience
To investigate the effects of sulphur dioxide on plant life

Skills involved
1. Fixing tube into seed box in correct position
2. Arranging support wires in correct position
3. Measuring quantities (liquids and solids)
4. Correct labelling of each part of the investigation
5. Observing and recording results

Unfamiliar words
Sulphur dioxide, pollute, damage, campden, seedlings, solution, crushed

Safety points
Pupils should be warned not to inhale the gases given off (from citric acid and campden tablets), particularly 'chesty' pupils.

General notes
1. Make sure that the compost is thoroughly moist before the experiment begins.
2. The groups carrying out this Activity should be allowed access to it for at least 7 days.
3. It is important that seedlings are given plenty of light but not direct sunlight.

4. Help with filling in the table may be necessary.

Apparatus list
Campden tablets
Citric acid solution
4 seed trays and seedlings
4 clear plastic bags
Some wire to make supports (needed to keep bag from touching small plants)
4 small glass tubes (ignition tubes)
String
2 teaspoons (or any other suitable item) for crushing tablets

Details for any construction
None

Activity 4:
Sulphur dioxide in fuels

Objective
Knowledge that sulphur dioxide gas is a product of burning certain fuels

Experience
To compare the amounts of sulphur dioxide produced when coal and coke are burnt

Skills involved
1. Setting up the apparatus as indicated in a diagram
2. Measuring a specified amount by weighing
3. Collecting and securing gases using plastic bags
4. Using and reading a Draeger tube
5. Observing and recording information

Unfamiliar words
Escape, crushed

Safety points
1. Make sure that when plastic bags are full of collected gases they are tightly closed.
2. Handle Draeger tubes carefully, particularly when the ends have been broken off.

General notes
Much discussion can follow the completion of this Activity, e.g. cities and smokeless zones, smoke and ill health.

Apparatus list
Hard glass test tubes (2)
Rubber bungs and delivery tubing bent as
    shown in diagram (page 10, pupils' book)
Retort stand and clamps
Bunsen burner
Crushed coal and coke
Plastic bags
Beaker
Ice
Draeger multigas detector kit
Draeger tubes for sulphur dioxide

Details for any construction
None

Activity 5:
Dirt on windows

Objective
Awareness of factors affecting amount of air
pollution

Experience
Measuring the amount of dust particles in the
air by scraping windows

Skills involved
1. Using a window scraper
2. Measuring the degree of pollution by
   'tracing paper' layering
3. Using and reading a compass
4. Collecting results and completing a table

Unfamiliar words
Scraper, compass, measuring, tracing,
completely, disappear

Safety points
1. Care must be taken when pressing on
   window with scraper.
2. Care must also be taken if steps have to be
   used when actually scraping the outside of
   windows.

General notes
1. Organisation is important here and pre-
   discussion will be necessary, e.g. how to
   read and use a compass, how to measure
   the area for scraping, and how to find the
   degree of pollution by paper layering.

2. The results will depend on the direction of
   the wind the day before.

Apparatus list
Scraper
Bulldog clip
Sheets of white paper
Sheets of tracing paper
Magnetic compass
Cardboard frames
Tape

Details for any construction
See diagram 28, page 126 for construction of
scraper.

Activity 6:
Can smoking harm the lungs?

Objective
Awareness that the smoke from cigarettes
contains harmful chemicals

Experience
Using a 'smoking machine' to show what
happens when 5 cigarettes are 'smoked'

Skills involved
1. Setting up and checking the apparatus
2. Finding the pH of solutions using universal
   indicator paper
3. Observing results and reactions and
   recording these
4. Making simple deductions

Unfamiliar words
Harmful, universal, indicator, alkaline, neutral

Safety points
1. Care must be taken when inserting and
   removing rubber bungs (U-tube and test
   tubes).
2. Do *not* allow pupils to remove the glass
   wool from the U-tube as part of the
   Activity.

General notes
1. This is obviously a useful Activity to
   introduce a discussion on the habit of
   smoking. It could be further developed to

investigate possible differences between different brands of cigarettes and also to consider 'King Size' cigarettes.
2. Ensure that the water is neutral before smoke is bubbled through.

Apparatus list
Smoking machine apparatus (see page 14, pupils' book)
Glass wool
5 cigarettes
Filter pump
Universal indicator paper

Details for any construction
None

Activity 7:
Noise in school

Objective
Awareness that noise is a form of pollution

Experience
Using a noise meter to measure noise levels in various parts of the school

Skills involved
1. Operating a noise meter
2. Reading the scale on a noise meter
3. Filling in a results table

Unfamiliar words
Decibels, dangerous, noise meter

Safety points
None

General notes
1. It is important that pupils realise the delicate nature of the noise meter, therefore careful instruction in its use must be given.
2. There is scope for extension of this Activity, particularly on methods of reducing noise.

Apparatus list
Noise meter
Clip board
A copy of the results table (see page 16, pupils' book)

Details for any construction
None

Activity 8:
Traffic noise

Objective
Awareness that noise is a form of pollution

Experience
Using a noise meter to measure traffic noise

Skills involved
1. Using a noise meter
2. Transferring information (from noise meter) to results table
3. Interpretation of results

Unfamiliar words
Measurements, noisier

Safety points
1. Ensure that pupils take care when out of school, particularly near traffic.
2. Check on consent forms.

General notes
1. Instructions will be needed on how to use noise meter and the care needed when handling it.
2. This Activity could be done on different days by different groups and results could then be compared.

Apparatus list
Noise meter
Camera (optional)
Clip board
Pen or pencil

Details for any construction
None

Activity 9:
Collecting samples of water

Objective
Familiarity with and development of techniques for collecting samples

Experience
Collecting samples of water from a river or stream

Skills involved
1. Correct labelling of bottles to be used
2. Method of actually collecting the samples of water

Unfamiliar words
Waterproof, sample, surface

Safety points
1. Special care is needed when pupils are near rivers, canals, etc.
2. Parental consent forms may be needed.
3. It is useful to carry a plastic container full of clean water and a small bottle of antiseptic solution, e.g. Savlon, so that pupils can swill their hands after dipping them into river or canal water.
4. See also the precautions listed under 'Water pollution', page 115.

General notes
1. Photography could be used with advantage here for recording places of interest and locations where samples were taken.
2. It is important to ensure that the bottles have been labelled correctly.

Apparatus list
4 screw top bottles
Waterproof labels
Waterproof pen
Ruler
Container for carrying clean water
Small bottle of Savlon
Towel and soap

Details for any construction
None

Activity 10:
Looking for life in the water

Objective
Familiarity with and development of techniques for collecting samples

Experience
Collecting samples of water from river, stream, etc. to estimate the population of living things

Skills involved
1. Method of using nets
2. Ability to recognise living things
3. Transferring observations to results table

Unfamiliar words
Surface, touch, columns

Safety points
1. See 'Safety points' for Activity 9.
2. Precautions when near rivers etc. should be fully discussed before field trip is undertaken.

General notes
1. It is essential that pupils understand the techniques of sampling before going to the actual site.
2. Discussion of group results is also important if sampling is to be properly understood.

Apparatus list
Pond dipping net
Plastic bowl
Clip board
Plain paper
Hand lens
Pencil
Material for washing hands (see 'Apparatus list' for Activity 9)

Details for any construction
None

Activity 11:
Looking at mud from the river

Objective
Familiarity with and development of techniques for collecting samples

Experience
Collecting samples of mud from river, stream, etc. in order to identify and estimate the kinds of animal found, if any

Skills involved

1. Method of using nets in mud
2. Identifying life in the mud
3. Using pictures and drawings as a means of identification
4. Observing and recording and correctly entering results

Unfamiliar words

Scraper, identification, compare

Safety points

1. See 'Safety points' for Activity 9.
2. Pupils should use rubber or plastic gloves and wooden scrapers when turning over mud in the bowl.

General notes

Since this Activity demands on the spot identification of aquatic animals some pre-visit discussion will be needed regarding how to use the pictures or keys in order to identify what has been found.

Apparatus list

Pond dipping net
Plastic bowl
Clip board
Plain paper
Hand lens
Pencil
Rubber/plastic gloves
Wooden scraper
Animal identification pictures (see 'Notes for teacher', Activity 11)

Details for any construction
None

Activity 12:
Testing the water samples for acidity

Objective

Awareness that environmental factors can affect the purity of natural waters

Experience

Testing the pH of the water (samples collected in Activity 9)

Skills involved

1. Using a teat pipette
2. Using universal indicator paper
3. Comparing colour changes on universal indicator paper with standards (i.e. using comparator booklet)
4. Transferring observations made to a results table
5. Interpreting results

Unfamiliar words

Acid, alkali, neutral, indicator, acidity, pipette, comparator papers, repeat

Safety points

1. See 'Safety points' for Activity 9.
2. Ensure that pupils wash their hands after testing the water.

General notes

1. The terms acid, alkali and neutral will need elaboration; pH numbers will also need to be explained.
2. The results of this Activity provide ample opportunity for discussion about the pollution of our rivers.

Apparatus list

Samples of water collected in Activity 9
Universal indicator paper
Comparator papers (chart)
Teat pipette

Details for any construction
None

Activity 13:
How dirty is the water?

Objective

Using qualitative methods of investigation to determine degrees of contamination

Experience

Filtering collected samples of water and using the deposit as an indicator of 'dirtiness'

Skills involved

1. Measuring a known quantity of water from sample (25 cm³), using a measuring cylinder

2. Comparing the colour of filter papers, after filtration, as an indicator of the condition of the water
3. Observing and recording results
4. Interpreting results

Unfamiliar words
Tripod, funnel, measure, underneath, slightly, condition, dirtiness

Safety points
After handling filter papers, hands should be thoroughly washed in soap and water

General notes
1. Some guidance will be needed to assist pupils on how to compare filter papers.
2. Discuss the results before questions are attempted.
3. Make sure the different samples are filtered into separate beakers.

Apparatus list
Measuring cylinder
Tripod
Filter papers
Filter funnel
Samples of water collected in Activity 9
Beaker

Details for any construction
None

Activity 14:
Are microbes in the water from the river?

Objective
Understanding the techniques of preparing a culture plate

Experience
Investigating the presence of microbes in river water using prepared agar plates

Skills involved
1. Preparing a culture dish for the incubator
2. Recognising 'groups' of microbes
3. Recording results
4. Interpreting results

Unfamiliar words
Agar plates, incubator, petri dish, microbes

Safety points
After the dish has been incubated it is important that pupils do not open the petri dishes (see 'Notes for teacher', Activity 14).

General notes
1. Why the incubator was used will need to be explained.
2. This Activity could be developed further; causes of river pollution and the dangers of swimming in such places are two possibilities for discussion.

Apparatus list
Filter papers from Activity 13
Prepared agar plates
Incubator
Sellotape
Chinagraph pencil or label (self-adhesive)
Scissors

Details for any construction
None

Activity 15:
Is garden fertiliser always useful?

Objective
Awareness that fertilisers can be harmful as well as useful

Experience
Growing seeds using varying amounts of fertiliser in the soil

Skills involved
1. Preparation of seed trays
2. Measuring correct amount of fertiliser
3. Correctly labelling trays
4. Observing and recording results
5. Interpreting results

Unfamiliar words
Sprinkle, fertiliser, examine, differences

Safety points
Hands must be washed if they have been in contact with fertiliser.

General notes

1. Growmore is a good general fertiliser to use, but there are others.
2. Washed river sand is useful for this Activity.
3. Smaller containers can be used if the number of groups is large, but the recommended amount of fertiliser should be reduced accordingly.
4. It is important while the seeds are germinating that they do not dry out. It is best to water them from the bottom, but they may be done from above if a hand sprayer is used.

Apparatus list

Sand
5 seed trays
Paper towels
Mustard or cress seeds
Labels (self-adhesive are best)
Fertiliser (general)
Plastic teaspoons
Beaker
A fine spray would be useful for watering

Details for any construction
None

Activity 16:
Litter in the streets

Objective

Appreciation that a thoughtless person can be rated as one of the worst pollution agents

Experience

Using part of the local environment to investigate causes of pollution

Skills involved

1. Using a simple camera
2. Sorting, weighing and estimating litter
3. Interpreting results

Unfamiliar words

Spring balance, camera, photographs

Safety points

1. The usual accepted codes of behaviour need to be exercised when out of school.
2. Use plastic disposable gloves and insist that hands are thoroughly washed after disposing of the rubbish collected.

General notes

The Activity provides a useful starting point for developing an interest in mounting a class or school display or exhibition on pollution generally.

Apparatus list

Plastic rubbish bags
Plastic gloves
Clip board
Pencil
Results sheets
Spring balances
Camera and film

Details for any construction
None

Answers to questions in pupils' book

A letter D indicates that the answer cannot be predicted, usually because it is dependent on the results of the class experiments.

Activity 1
1. Red
2. Bright red
3. Dark red
4. Yes
5. No

Activity 2
1. D

Activity 3
1. Yes
2. Tray 1
3. In great amounts, yes; in small amounts, no. In fact, in small amounts the gas can be beneficial.

Activity 4
1. It shows how you can lessen the amount of smoke but not the amount of sulphur dioxide given off. Results and answers will be variable depending on the smokeless fuel used.

Activity 5
1-4 D; Depends on wind direction on the day before the scraping was made

Activity 6
1. Mainly tar
2. Neutral
3. Acid

Activity 7
1, 2 D
3. carpets, yes; woodblock flooring, no; curtains, yes; cork tiles, yes; plastic tiles, no. Rubber; Coconut matting; Foam rubber padding (e.g. under desk lids)

Activity 8
1. D

Activity 12
1-6 D

Activity 13
1. D
2. Different animals and plants need different kinds of water to live in. For example, water shrimps will be found in clear running water but water lice will not; in still, stagnant water the reverse will be true.

Activity 14
1-7 D

Activity 15
1. A and B
2. E
3. Yes
4. Adding too much fertiliser

Activity 16
1-3 D

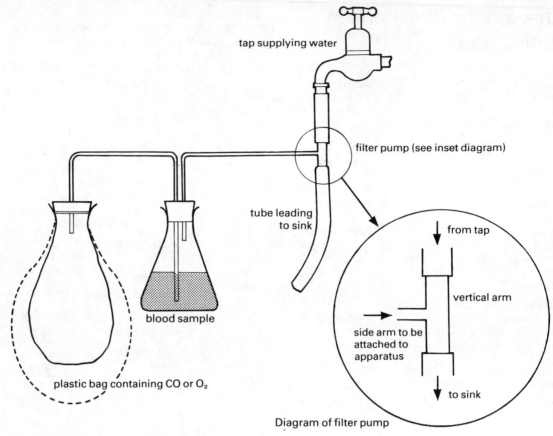

tap supplying water

filter pump (see inset diagram)

tube leading
to sink

blood sample

from tap

vertical arm

side arm to be
attached to
apparatus

to sink

Diagram of filter pump

plastic bag containing CO or O_2

DIAGRAM 26. Setup for bubbling gases through the blood sample.

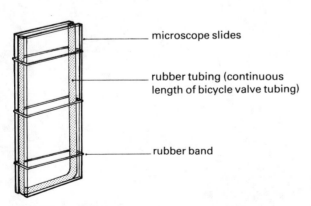

microscope slides

rubber tubing (continuous length of bicycle valve tubing)

rubber band

DIAGRAM 27. Construction of narrow flat container for detection of colour changes in the blood.

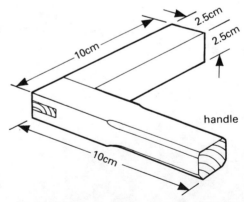

2.5cm

2.5cm

10cm

handle

10cm

DIAGRAM 28. Construction of wooden scraper (Activity 5).

Safe Eating

Summary of contents

The Unit attempts to highlight the importance of safe methods of food preservation and the dangers of ignoring food hygiene. The pupils are introduced to a simple microbe — yeast. Other microbes are considered and the awareness of the consequences of eating bad food is forceably presented. An investigation on how we can stop microbes growing on food is followed by detailed instructions on how to preserve food by heating, freezing and the use of chemicals.

A check-up at the end of the Unit tests what should have been learnt about the best ways of preserving food.

Equipment list for whole of Unit

To be made
None

To be bought or obtained from other departments
Dried yeast
Sugar
Cooking salt
Pieces of muslin
Campden tablets
Vinegar
Freezing bags
Ties for bags
Fermentation locks
Rubber bungs (to accept fermentation locks and to fit boiling tubes)
Drinking straws
Bread
Meat
Fruit
Vegetables
Milk (pasteurised, sterilised, U.H.T., evaporated)

Tape recorder
Large sheets of paper for painting on
Paints, crayons, felt pens
China blue lactose agar
Resazurin dye
Screw top preserving jars
Plastic bowls
Plastic basins
Saucepans

To be collected
Table knives
Baking tray
Newspaper

Assumed normally available in laboratory
Microscopes
Microscope slides
Microscope cover slips
Teat pipettes
Mounting needles (or long pins)
Spatulas
Boiling tubes
Limewater
Thermometers (0-110°C)
Beakers (100 cm³, 250 cm³ and 400 cm³)
Test tubes
Test tube rack
Ice
Olive oil
Plastic gloves
Hand lens
Tweezers
Petri dishes
Sellotape
Chinagraph pencils
Bunsen burners
Tripod stands
Gauze squares
Heat resistant mats

Plastic syringes (2 cm³)
Measuring cylinders
Stop clocks
Rubber bungs to fit test tubes
Common salt
Mortar and pestle
Balance
Glass stirring rod
Elastic bands
Gummed labels
Availability of a refrigerator
Access to oven

Forward planner

Activity number	Advanced planning needed	Approximate Activity time (40 min period)	Are results of a previous Activity necessary?
1	Prepare yeast suspension (needs to be done the day before — see 'Apparatus list', Activity 1). Damp bread, meat, apple to be hung in polythene bag the week before (see page 2 of pupils' book)	1 period	No
2	Prepare ice and boiled water	Double period	No
3	Ensure that fresh and bad/mouldy foods and sour milk are available (allow food to go bad the week before)	1-2 periods	Activity 1
4	None. If a tape recorder is being used then pre-recorded tapes of 'cuttings' will need to be prepared	Double period	No
5	Prepare agar plates (see 'Notes for teacher'). Retain samples of fresh and bad food from Activity 3	Double period + single period 2 days later to fill in results	Activity 3
6	Prepare china blue lactose agar (see 'Notes for teacher'). Obtain fresh and sour milk	Single period + double period 1-2 days later to obtain all results	No
7	Prepare microbes growing on agar plates (see 'Notes for teacher')	Single period + double period 2-3 days later for results	No
8	Obtain fresh milk and milk 2, 3 and 4 days old	2-3 periods	No
9	Sterilise test tubes — each group will need 8 tubes. Collect several kinds of milk	3 periods + 1-2 periods 2 days later for testing and results	Activity 8
10	Set up control (see page 22 of pupils' book). Wash and prepare fruit and vegetables. (Preheat oven for Activity 14)	1 period	No
11		1 period	No
12		1 period	No
13		1 period	No
14		Double period	No
15		Double period*	No

* This Activity consists of 2 parts. If the class is broken down into 2 groups the approximate time required for the Activity is 1 period

Notes for teacher

It is important to remember that when using this Unit extra care should be taken with the handling of apparatus. Some useful and helpful suggestions will be found in the D.E.S. literature on 'Safety in laboratories'.

Some commonsense precautions

1. If any bacterial culture is dropped, it must be washed off with a solution of lysol — wear plastic gloves.
2. Hands should be washed before and after practical work.
3. Food (except that for experiments) or sweets should not be brought into the laboratory.
4. Any labels to be used should be wetted with a damp cloth **not licked.**
5. After use, prepared agar plates should not be opened by pupils. If plastic, they should be destroyed; if glass, they should be carefully opened wearing rubber gloves under a solution of 10% lysol and left for a few days.

Note: Much of this Unit will be of interest to home economics teachers and pupils, but Activities using bad or infected food should not be performed where other food is prepared, cooked, stored or eaten. These Activities are labelled 'Care' or 'Science lab only'.

In some of the Activities several groups will be working independently. It is therefore important that each group knows exactly what it should be doing. Discussion here is important. It is equally important that when results have been obtained by the individual groups, this information should be collated and made known to all groups.

Activity 2

The fact that yeast can respire anaerobically was deliberately not raised in the pupils' book because it could make the theory too difficult. Anaerobic respiration takes place over a longer time, but it is possible the yeast in tube e could be found to be producing carbon dioxide for this reason.

Activity 3

In preparing the materials (bad foods) for this Activity it is necessary to use extra strong polythene bags. This Activity must not be carried out in the home economics room.

Activity 4

If facilities allow, it is a good idea to pre-record the 'newspaper cuttings'. These would be useful for poor readers.

Before pupils attempt to answer the questions in this Activity, it is important to discuss the following safety points:
(a) why food taken from a deep freezer must be thoroughly thawed before cooking;
(b) that when cooking food a temperature of 100°C should be reached throughout it, to kill bacteria present;
(c) that although food may have been cooked properly it can still become infected later by careless handling.

Activity 5

Prepared nutrient agar plates are required for this Activity. Use the following procedure to make the nutrient agar solution for the plates. Weigh out 5 g nutrient agar. Add 180 cm³ distilled water in a 250 cm³ flask. Shake well, then leave for 15 min or until agar has dissolved. Plug neck of flask with cotton wool, place in autoclave or pressure cooker and sterilise for 15 min at 1 kg/cm² (15 lb/sq in). Remove from heat and allow to cool to 45°C. Pour into sterilised petri dish until dish is about half full. To preserve sterility as much as possible the neck of the flask should be flamed before pouring the agar, and the lid of the petri dish should be tilted on one side just enough to pour in the agar; it should not be completely removed nor should it touch the bench.

Store and incubate the plates upside down to reduce contamination and prevent condensation on the lid falling on to the agar. *Note:* the quantity suggested will make up to 18 agar plates.

Careful control must be exercised with this Activity. Pupils must know exactly what they are doing and the precautions they must take. Under no circumstances must the bad food be touched with the fingers. All forceps must be well flamed before and after use. It is good practice to see that pupils wash their hands thoroughly when they have finished the Activity.

Activity 6

Prepared china blue lactose agar is required for this Activity. Make up the china blue agar as the ordinary agar (Activity 5) but do not pour into petri dishes. Instead half fill McCartney bottles with the solution. When needed the bottles can be placed in a water bath, in order to melt the agar, and maintained at 45-50°C until ready for use.

Activity 7

This Activity requires prepared plates with microbes growing on the nutrient agar. Prepare the agar plates as for Activity 5. When the agar is set, inoculate each plate with *Bacillus subtilis* and then incubate for 24 hours. (*Bacillus subtilis* can be obtained from recognised biological suppliers.) See D.E.S. Pamphlet No 61 'The use of micro-organisms in schools' Appendix 2.

The microbes should not grow in the halves of the plates containing bleach, disinfectant, strong salt solution, strong sugar solution, vinegar, campden solution, smoke and the one placed in the refrigerator. Weak sugar solution should encourage the growth of microbes.

An extension to Activity 7 could be to show that although the plate taken from the refrigerator did not show additional growth, once removed and placed somewhere warm, growth will begin on it again.

Activity 8

It is important when carrying out this Activity to (a) allow the milk to remain at room temperature for the suggested number of days and (b) pre-heat the milk to a temperature of about 40°C in a water bath or incubator just prior to the start of the lesson. This is necessary because the resazurin test will not work below 37°C. The colour of the dye changes from blue to pink then colourless depending on the degree of sourness of the milk. Resazurin solution is made by dissolving one tablet in 50 cm³ of distilled water.

Activities 9-15 (preserving food)

It is an advantage if all the seven Activities can be carried out at the same time by the class working in groups. The method of grouping must be left to the teacher since this will depend largely on the size and ability of the class. It may be more convenient, in terms of organisation, to consider Activity 15 as requiring two groups, since this Activity is in two parts.

Before groups are allowed to begin carrying out their various tasks, it may be wise for the teacher to demonstrate the techniques involved, and then any special skill required could be highlighted.

Some suggestions and precautions for Activities 10-15 are given below:
1. Suitable fruits and vegetables are apples, gooseberries, plums, damsons and sliced beans.
2. It is better to use fresh materials, but if these are not available frozen foods can be substituted, provided they are completely thawed out before use. (Do not allow pupils to eat these in this condition.)
3. All apparatus must be thoroughly clean and fruit and vegetables properly prepared.
4. Kilner jars are usually sterilised by holding them with a cloth over the spout of a boiling kettle — the teacher should do this.
5. Lids can be sterilised by pouring boiling water over them.

It is important to emphasise that not all the methods of preservation are suitable for all the foods they are tried on. This should be brought out by class discussion each time different preservation methods are tested by the experiments. The Activities are not intended to be cook book recipes; they are scientific investigations into suitable and unsuitable ways of preserving food. Eating of any of the sucessfully bottled foods or jams must be left to the discretion of the teacher. Obviously deciding factors will be:
1. The cleanliness of the apparatus used
2. Was the method of preserving correctly carried out?
3. Was the class organisation and discipline o' an acceptable standard when tasks were being carried out?

If there is any doubt, the food should not be eaten.

At the end of this section further discussion of other methods of preserving food by examination of commercial products could be a useful exercise.

Main objectives and ideas

Main objectives
1. Awareness that microbes can cause food to go bad and that contaminated or bad food can result in food poisoning
2. To learn ways of preventing food from going bad

Key ideas
1. What microbes are
2. What microbes need in order to grow
3. How to prevent microbes growing
4. Methods of preserving food (freezing, salting, pickling, sulphur dioxide, bottling, jamming)

Information for each Activity

Activity 1:
Looking at a microbe

Objective
Awareness that microbes are living things

Experience
Using a microscope to see yeast growing

Skills involved
1. Preparing a microscope slide using live yeast liquid
2. Using a microscope
3. Understanding $\times 10$, $\times 20$ and $\times 40$ with reference to the lens power of a microscope

Unfamiliar words
Pipette, cover slip

Safety points
None

General notes
1. Explain the meaning of $\times 10$, $\times 20$ and $\times 40$ with reference to the lens power of a microscope.
2. Cover slips must be put on to slides correctly to prevent air bubbles forming.

Apparatus list
Live yeast liquid
Microscope
Microscope slide
Cover slips
Teat pipette
2 long pins or mounting needles

Details for any construction
No construction, but live yeast liquid must be made beforehand. First make a yeast suspension using
½ teaspoon of dried yeast
10 cm³ water
1 teaspoonful of sugar
Incubate the mixture in a flask overnight at a temperature of 32°C. Also put 25 cm³ of water into the incubator.

Before the lesson add 1 cm³ of the yeast suspension to the 25 cm³ of water.

Activity 2:
Finding out what yeast needs to grow

Objective
Awareness that yeast is a microbe

Experience
Conditions needed for yeast to grow

Skills involved
1. Reading and carrying out instructions
2. Measuring required quantities
3. Pouring limewater into fermentation lock

Unfamiliar words
Fermentation lock, anaerobic

Safety points
None

General notes

1. Since there are five groups working at the same time, it is important that each group knows exactly what to do.
2. Each group must be aware of the results of other groups in order to complete the last entry in the results table.

Apparatus list

Spatula (5)
Dried yeast (5)
Dry sugar or glucose (4)
Fermentation lock with rubber bung — bung should fit boiling tube (5)
Boiling tube (5)
Limewater (5)
0-110°C thermometer (4)
Beaker, 250 cm³ (5)
Straws (qs)
Test tube (5)
Hot water (qs)
Ice (1)
Olive oil (1)
Boiled water (1)
Note: numbers in brackets indicate the number of items needed for five groups — these will be working at the same time.

Details for any construction
No construction, but fermentation locks must be fitted with the correct bung before the start of the lesson.

Activity 3:
What can microbes do to food? (Science lab only)

Objective
A knowledge of what microbes can do

Experience
To recognise differences between good and bad food

Skills involved
To observe and record observations

Unfamiliar words
Mouldy

132

Safety points

1. Do not allow pupils to handle bad food.
2. If there is a risk that they may handle food which is bad, they must wear plastic or rubber gloves. (Pupils should be told why this precaution is necessary.)

General notes
Pupils may need some help in recording the 'properties' of fresh and bad foods.

Apparatus list
Fresh bread
Fresh meat
Fresh fruit
Fresh milk
Stale bread
Bad meat
Bad fruit
Sour milk
} see 'Forward planner' (use only small quantities of food which is intended to go bad)
Plastic gloves
Hand lens
Plastic bags (strong)

Details for any construction
None

Activity 4:
What harm can microbes on food do?

Objective
To increase an awareness of the source and dangers of food poisoning

Experience
Listening to (or reading about) major food poisoning outbreaks and their consequences

Skills involved

1. Ability to listen (or read about) food poisoning and to discuss and interpret the consequences
2. To use the imagination to draw an eye-catching poster relating to food poisoning and how it may by prevented

Unfamiliar words
Alert, writhing, contaminated, bacterium (bacteria), symptoms

Safety points
None

General notes
1. This Activity needs to be followed by carefully planned discussion.
2. Use any current news item(s) which may be relevant to this topic.

Apparatus list
Tape recorder
Pre-recorded tape of newspaper clippings
Sheets of paper for poster design
Paints or crayons

Details for any construction
None

General notes
1. Before carrying out this Activity read 'Forward planner' and 'Notes for teacher'.
2. Although methods of preparation of the plates are explained, it is important that pupils are guided through each of the stages in the preparation of the plates.

Apparatus list
Tweezers (metal)
3 nutrient agar plates
Sellotape
Chinagraph pencil
Bunsen burner
Heat resistant mat
Samples of fresh and bad foods (from Activity 3)

Details for any construction
None

Activity 5:
Growing the microbes which make food bad (Science lab only)

Objective
An awareness that given the right environments microbes will grow rapidly

Experience
1. Growing microbes under control conditions
2. To give a visual image of some colonies of microbes on bad food

Skills involved
1. Labelling agar plates correctly
2. Transferring samples of the food to the plates
3. Sterilising tweezers
4. Sealing the plates correctly

Unfamiliar words
Nutrient agar

Safety points
1. Bad food should never be handled. It is most important that pupils understand the reasons for this.
2. All contaminated plates must be sterilised before being disposed of.

Activity 6:
Growing the microbes which make milk go sour

Objective
Extending knowledge on growing microbes

Experience
Providing the right conditions for growing microbes in milk

Skills involved
1. Correct way of labelling dishes
2. Correct way of sterilising neck of agar bottle
3. Following detailed instructions on the preparation of plates
4. Observing and recording observations

Unfamiliar words
Lactose, patches of microbes, china blue lactose agar

Safety points
It is most important that pupils are well informed about the dangers of handling bad or contaminated food.

General notes

1. Use fresh pasteurised milk.
2. Make up china blue agar as ordinary agar (see 'Notes for teacher').

Apparatus list

2 petri dishes (sterilised before use)
Fresh milk
Sour milk
Dropping pipette
Sellotape
Chinagraph pencil
2 bottles of melted china blue lactose agar, cooled to 50°C (see 'Notes for teacher')

Details for any construction
None

Activity 7:
How can we stop microbes growing on food? (Science lab only)

Objective

Knowledge that there are certain substances which can be used to prevent food going bad

Experience

That although many substances can be used to prevent things going bad only a few can be used with foods

Skills involved

1. Labelling plate according to given instructions
2. Adding the suggested substances in the right place
3. Observing and interpreting results

Unfamiliar words

Disinfectant, campden tablets, sulphur dioxide, incubate

Safety points

It must be made quite clear to the pupils that they must not touch the *inside* of the plate.

General notes

1. It is important that nutrient agar plates should not be exposed too long to the air

after pupils have added required solutions and sealed the lids of the plates.
2. Incubate treated plates upside down (this prevents condensation) for 24 hours.
3. See 'Notes for teacher' for preparation of plates.

Apparatus list

Prepared nutrient agar plates with microbes growing on the jelly (see 'Notes for teacher') (10)
Chinagraph pencil or label (10)
Fine pipette (8)
Note: Numbers in brackets indicate the number of items needed for 10 experiments.

Details for any construction
None

Activity 8:
Testing the freshness of milk

Objective

Knowledge of how to test for the freshness of milk

Experience

Carrying out several methods for the testing of the freshness of milk

Skills involved

1. Preparation of the samples of milk for each test
2. Correct way to use a syringe
3. Observing and recording results

Unfamiliar words

Clotted, resazurin

Safety points

Care must be taken when bringing the milk to the boil and when removing the beaker in order to pour the milk into the test tube.

General notes

1. Read 'Forward planner'.
2. Resazurin changes from blue to pink to colourless. The rate of change depends upon the degree of sourness.

3. All milk used for the resazurin test should be warmed to 37°C (see 'Notes for teacher').

Apparatus list (for each group)
Method 1
Fresh milk
Milk that is 2, 3 and 4 days old
100 cm³ beaker
4 test tubes labelled 1, 2, 3 and 4
Heat resistant mat
Burner
Tripod
Gauze
Test tube rack

Method 2
Fresh milk
Milk that is 1, 2, 3 and 4 days old
4 test tubes labelled 1, 2, 3 and 4
Test tube rack
Resazurin dye solution (made by dissolving *one* tablet in 50 cm³ of distilled water)
2 cm³ plastic syringe
Measuring cylinder
Stop clock

Details for any construction
None

Activity 9:
Testing some food preservatives on milk

Objective
Awareness that there are many ways of preserving milk

Experience
Finding out the most effective way of preserving milk

Skills involved
1. Preparation of test tubes
   (a) Correct labelling
   (b) ¾ filling each with a particular kind of milk
   (c) Carrying out specific instructions for each of the eight test tubes
2. Observing and recording results
3. Carrying out 'clotting' and 'resazurin' tests

Unfamiliar words
None

Safety points
Campden tablets and acid give off sulphur dioxide — careful smelling of the tube containing these tablets is required.

General notes
All test tubes used for these tests must be sterilised in an oven at 100°C or in boiling water.

Apparatus list (for each group)
8 clean test tubes
6 rubber stoppers
Test tube rack
Campden tablets
Vinegar
Salt (common salt)
Muslin squares
Elastic bands
Labels
Dropping pipette
Spatula
A selection of milks:
(a) fresh pasteurised
(b) boiled fresh pasteurised
(c) sterilised
(d) U.H.T.
(e) evaporated (diluted)
Availability of:
(a) refrigerator
(b) pestle and mortar

The following are needed after 2 days (for the 'clotting' and 'resazurin' tests)
100 cm³ beakers
Bunsen burner
Tripod
Wire gauze
Heat resistant mat
Resazurin dye solution
2 cm³ plastic syringe
Stop clock

Details for any construction
None

Activity 10:
Freezing

Objective
Investigation into possible ways of preserving food

Experience
Finding out if freezing, as a method of preserving food, can be used for both fruit and vegetables

Skills involved
Correct method of preparing food for freezing

Unfamiliar words
Polythene, compartment

Safety points
None

General notes
1. See that bags are correctly labelled and sealed.
2. In discussion bring out the differences between using a proper freezer and using the freezing compartment of a refrigerator.

Apparatus list
Balance
Fruit (peeled and cut into slices) e.g. apples
Vegetables (peeled if necessary and cut into slices)
2 polythene bags with ties
Labels
Availability of freezing compartment of refrigerator

Details for any construction
None

Activity 11:
Salt and sugar

Objective
Investigation into possible ways of preserving food

Experience
To find out if salt and sugar can be used to preserve vegetables and fruit

Skills involved
1. Preparing fruit and vegetables for preserving
2. Correct layering of fruit or vegetables in the jars with the sugar or salt

Unfamiliar words
None

Safety points
None

General notes
1. It is important that the jars have been thoroughly cleaned before use.
2. Fruit and vegetables should be carefully washed.
3. Salt and sugar preserve by dehydrating the food and by forming a strong solution that microbes cannot tolerate.

Apparatus list
Fruit
Vegetables
Cooking salt
Sugar
2 screw top jars
Labels
Knife   ⎫ if pupils prepare the fruit
Basin   ⎬ and vegetables themselves
Small bowl ⎭

Details for any construction
None

Activity 12:
Pickling

Objective
Investigation into possible ways of preserving food

Experience
To find out if vinegar can be used for preserving both vegetables and fruit

Skills involved
1. Preparing vegetables and fruit for pickling
2. Reading and carrying out written instructions, as for other Activities

Unfamiliar words
None

Safety points
None

General notes
As for Activity 11.

Apparatus list
Fruit
Vegetables
2 screw top jars
Vinegar
Beaker
Labels
Knife
Basin   } if pupils prepare the fruit
Small bowl } and vegetables themselves

Details for any construction
None

Activity 13:
Sulphur dioxide as a preservative

Objective
Investigation into possible ways of preserving food

Experience
Finding out if sulphur dioxide (SO_2) can be used to preserve fruit

Skills involved
1. Correct way to use pestle and mortar
2. Making a campden solution from crushed campden tablets

Unfamiliar words
Campden tablet, sulphur dioxide, mortar and pestle

Safety points
Campden tablets in contact with acid (fruit juice) give off sulphur dioxide which can cause irritation to eyes, nose and throat. If prolonged, exposure can even affect breathing.

General notes
1. It is important that the lid is placed on the jar immediately after adding the campden solution.

2. Because the SO_2 is soon lost, campden tablets are not a sufficiently strong preservative on their own.

Apparatus list
Fruit
Campden tablets
Mortar and pestle
Measuring cylinder
400 cm³ beaker
2 screw top jars
Stirring rod
Labels
Knife
Basin   } if pupils prepare the fruit
Small bowl } themselves

Details for any construction
None

Activity 14:
Bottling

Objective
Investigation into possible ways of preserving food

Experience
To find out if bottling, as a means of preserving food, can be used for fruit

Skills involved
1. Preparing kilner jars with fruit
2. Preparing syrup
3. Method of handling hot jars
4. Some measuring skills needed

Unfamiliar words
Kilner jar, lever balance, sterilise

Safety points
1. Care must be taken when handling very hot jars.
2. Care must be taken when pouring boiling liquids into containers.
3. When taking jars out of the oven extreme care is needed.

General notes
1. To sterilise kilner jars hold the jar over the spout of a boiling kettle for about 1 min.
2. Use a good cloth or oven gloves.

Apparatus list
Access to an oven
Boiling water
2 kilner jars (sterilised)
Fruit
Baking tray
Newspaper
Measuring cylinder
Lever balance
Sugar
Teaspoon
Saucepan
Labels

Details for any construction
None

Activity 15:
Jamming

Objective
Investigation into possible ways of preserving food

Experience
To find out if the method used for jamming in order to preserve fruit can also be used for preserving vegetables

Skills involved
1. Similar to Activity 14
2. Technique of skimming off scum from the jam

Unfamiliar words
Wrinkle, scum, waxed paper discs

Safety points
1. Make sure fruit and vegetables have been thoroughly washed.
2. Care must be taken when pouring very hot jam into jars.
3. Care must be taken when handling hot jars — use oven gloves if possible.

General notes
1. When results are examined after 2 weeks, class discussion will be needed to decide if the processes have really been successful and practical.
2. Criteria should be 'looking' and 'smelling'; tasting must be left to the discretion of the teacher (see 'Notes for teacher').

Apparatus list
Fruit (washed)
Vegetables (washed)
Balance
Sugar
Measuring cylinder
2 saucepans
2 wooden spoons
Jam pots
Jam pot covers
Gas ring
Cup
Labels
2 heat resistant mats

Details for any construction
None

Answers to questions in pupils' book

A letter D indicates that the answer cannot be predicted, usually because it is dependent on the results of the class experiments.

Activity 1
1. Yes
2. × 40
3. Yes
4. Diagrams should show the yeast 'budding', i.e. a small bulge appearing from the side of one cell and growing to the same size as that cell.

Activity 2
1. In experiment a
2. It turns it cloudy.
3. Carbon dioxide
4. In experiment a
5. There were bubbles.
6. Air, water, food and warmth

Activity 4
1. Cover it carefully with waterproof dressing.
2. Thaw it properly before cooking.
3. No, some are not.
4. Stomach pains, diarrhoea, sickness
5. *Staphylococcus, Bacillus cereus, Salmonella hadar*
6. Ham, potato, turkey, potato salad and many others
7. It can be fatal. It is passed on easily by infected food.

Activity 5
1. There are more on the bad foods.
2. D
3. No
4. To kill any microbes already on them
5. To find out which microbes are on the food

Activity 6
1. Pale blue
2. Pale blue
3. Pale blue with dark blue patches
4. The sour milk
5. Yes
6. A dairy or milk inspector, to see if the milk is clean and fresh

Activity 7
1. A jelly with food in for microbes
2. To see their effect compared with the untreated side
3. Sulphur dioxide
4. 8, 9 and possibly 10
5. 1, 2, 3, 4, 6, 7
6. Plate 5
7. Bleach, disinfectant, campden tablets
8. They are poisonous
9. 1. Salt
   2. Strong sugar solution
   3. Sugar
   4. Vinegar
   5. Smoke
   6. No water, sulphur dioxide
   7. Refrigerator (no warmth)

Activity 8
Questions: page 17
1. 4
2. 4, possibly 3
3. Yes
4. No
5. Yes
Questions: page 18
1. The milk in tube 4
2. Yes, tube 4 (maybe 3)
3. Yes, tube 1
4. Yes

Activity 9
1. Air, microbes, dust
2. Air, microbes
3. Dust, and microbes not already in
4. D (probably 1, 2, 3, 6)

5. Refrigerator, campden tablets, salt, sugar
6. Campden tablets and salt would taste odd.
7. D (probably U.H.T. or sterilised)
8. D (probably U.H.T. or evaporated)

Activities 10-15
1. Bananas, lettuce, milk (it separates). Mostly because they go soft and horrible when thawed out.
2. Fish and savoury foods like beans
3. Vegetables, especially onions, beetroot
4. No, some does not have enough pectin so it would not set
5. No. They would taste too sweet and be runny.
6. Use a coin (to release vacuum, to let in air).
7. Air
8. We would have little or no fruit in winter, and no food from abroad.
9. Glass jars might break.
10. *Salmonella, Staphylococcus, Bacillus cereus*
11. Those that live without air
12. Yes. Because they can live without air. So the food must be sterilised first.
13. Typhoid, botulism
14. Tropical, hot countries. It is difficult to keep everything cool. Microbes multiply in the heat.
15. Greenland, Finland, Iceland. It is always cold in these countries.

Science at Home

Summary of contents

Does insulating material in the loft of a house really keep the house warmer? Does double glazing help to keep the heat in a warm room from escaping to the outside? These are questions that the first few Activities in the Unit attempt to answer. A 'best buy' is also investigated regarding floor tiles. Do they dent easily? Do they stain? Would they burn if near a flame? Biological detergents, and detergents generally, are used extensively for household cleaning. Are they really better than soap? Do they remove stains? Again, pupils are encouraged to try to find answers through carefully selected Activities.

Equipment list for whole of Unit

To be made
Polystyrene discs, to stand beakers on and to cover beakers (Activity 3)
Wooden base approximately 40 × 40 cm (Activity 4)
Tilt measuring board (Activity 7)
Rubber shoe sole to be stuck to a 1 kg mass (Activity 7)

To be bought or obtained from other departments
Floor tiles (as many different varieties as possible)
Household bleach
90 cm length of metal tube (electrical conduit is ideal)
Centre punch (must fit metal tubing)
Colouring (food dyes)
Eggs
Collection of washing powders (i.e. different enzyme and non-enzyme detergents)

Liquid soft soap

To be collected
Polystyrene soap cups
Polystyrene tiles
Plasticine
Felt underlay
House bricks
Household liquids, e.g. blackcurrant juice, coffee, tea, ink, food dyes (for staining)
White material (cotton or linen)
Substances for staining tiles, e.g. egg yolk, gravy, beer, tomato sauce, coffee, tea, cocoa
Plastic teaspoon

Assumed normally available in laboratory
Thermometers
Beakers (50 cm³, 100cm³, 150 cm³ tall form, 400 cm³ squat form, 600 cm³)
Stop clock
Heat resistant mats
Retort stands and clamps
Test tubes and test tube racks
Measuring cylinder
Dropping tubes
Plastic syringe (1 cm³)
Cardboard
Rubber bands
Felt pens (red, green and blue)
String
Magnifying glass
Soap solution
Liquid detergents
Soft water
Hard water
Sodium sesquicarbonate crystals
Dilute hydrochloric acid
Pepsin powder
Spatula
Scissors

Forward planner

Activity number	Advanced planning needed	Approximate Activity time (40 min period)	Are results of a previous Activity necessary?
1	Drill holes in polystyrene beakers and cardboard sheet	2 periods + 1 period	No
2	None	2 periods + 1 period	Activity 1
3	Cut discs from polystyrene tiles to cover and to stand beakers on	2 periods + 1 period	Activities 1 and 2
4	Collect a variety of floor tiles. Cut some 3 cm × 3 cm squares from new and worn tiles. For Activity 7 make hinged tilt measuring board and stick shoe sole to 1 kg mass	1 period ⎫	No
5		1 period ⎪ Best attempted	Activity 4
6		1 period ⎬ as a circus of	No
7		1 period ⎪ experiments	No
8		1 period ⎪	No
9		1 period ⎭	No
10	None	1 period	Activities 4-9
11	Prepare hard and soft water. Prepare detergent solution	2 periods	No
12	None	1 period	Activity 11
13	Prepare hard water	1 period	Activity 12
14	Obtain the white from hard boiled egg	1 period + 1 period a few days later	No
15	Collect different detergents	1 period + 1 period a few days later	No
16	Collect substances stated in list (egg yolk, beer, tomato sauce, tea, coffee, etc.). Cut white material (cotton, linen) into 5 cm × 5 cm squares	1 period	No
17	Retain stained material from Activity 16	2 periods	Activity 16

Notes for teacher

A convenient way of introducing the topic of heat insulation is by discussion, such as 'How can we save energy, particularly in the home?'

Activity 1
Before the pupils are allowed to start this Activity, it is important that the model 'house' is displayed and its parts explained. The setting up of the apparatus should also be carefully discussed. An electric kettle is found to be the best means of supplying the boiling water. Collecting the data is fairly straightforward, but pupils may need some instruction on how to enter results in the table. When the class has completed Activity 1, it will be necessary to explain carefully and slowly how to 'fill in' the graph and, equally important, how to interpret the completed graph.

Activity 2
This will need a similar teaching strategy. If time permits, other kinds of insulating material could be used.

Activity 3
Similar organisation to Activities 1 and 2 is needed here and 'who does what' in the group must be decided upon before the Activity is started. Some pupils may need help in interpreting the results/graph in order to answer the questions on page 11.

Activites 4-10
It may be a useful teaching point to mention *Which?* reports and explain what this means and what has to be done before the report can be written. Remind pupils that they will be asked to produce a similar report (page 21, pupils' book).

Regarding the organisation of Activities 4-9, it may be better to have two duplicate sets of apparatus arranged as two independent circus systems. The depth of penetration (Activity 9) may prove a little difficult for some. A class discussion may be needed here to explore possible ways of doing this. After each group has completed its investigations and made its report, an attempt should be made to obtain a class consensus of opinion on the best type of tile for any particular room in the home. Where differences are expressed, further discussions might be useful.

Activities 11-17
These should be fairly straightforward. The main difficulty may be in the skill needed to measure the suggested quantities of soap and detergent solution and the accurate recording of results.

Since some of these experiments need preparation (e.g. Activites 14 and 16) and then leaving for a few days, some convenient storage space will be needed. In some cases, when carrying out investigations, a control experiment is set up (see Activity 15). It is important that the pupils understand the significance of a control in this context.

Main objectives and ideas

Main objectives
1. Awareness that if certain alterations are made in houses, a great amount of heat energy can be conserved
2. Appreciation that there is a need to save energy
3. Ability to investigate problems scientifically
4. Willingness to examine critically claims made by manufacturers of certain household items
5. Recognition of the importance of discussion, both at class level and group level, in helping to solve problems and in the interpretation of results

Key ideas
1. Ways of saving heat energy in the home
2. Loft insulation and double glazing are methods which can be used to prevent heat loss in the home
3. Floor tiles vary in their composition, e.g. plastic, cork, wood, carpet type and ceramic. Do they stand up to the wear and tear of everyday use as claimed by the manufacturers?
4. Detergents as dirt and stain removers. Comparing soap and detergents. Are biological detergents more effective?

Information for each Activity

Activity 1:
Does heat move?

Objective
Awareness that heat energy can be transferred

Experience
Using a model house to investigate heat movement

Skills involved

1. Setting up the model house
2. Transferring boiling water from a kettle or similar container to the beaker
3. Reading a thermometer
4. Entering readings correctly in a results table
5. Filling in the graph
6. Interpreting the graph

Unfamiliar words

Polystyrene, thermometer, temperature, plasticine, rate

Safety points

1. It is important that thermometers are properly secured by the plasticine.
2. Care must be taken in transferring boiling water, e.g. from kettle to beaker.

General notes

1. Since several operations need to be done at the same time, i.e. temperature reading of top and bottom thermometers and the entering of these results, it is important that each group member knows exactly what to do.
2. Pupils will need help in filling in the graph — this part of the Activity cannot be rushed.
3. Discussion about what the graph shows is important. This needs to be done before the questions are attempted.

Apparatus list

2 thermometers
Beaker (600 cm³)
Polystyrene beaker
Sheet of cardboard to cover top of beaker
Stop clock
Polystyrene tile
Rubber bands
Plasticine (approx 250 g)
Felt underlay (approx 50 × 10 cm)
Felt pens (1 red and 1 green)
Scissors (if felt and cardboard are not cut to size)

Details for any construction
None

Activity 2:
Will felt stop heat from moving?

Objective

Ability to understand problems and to attempt ways of solving them when certain instructions are given

Experience

Using model house to investigate ways of preventing heat loss

Skills involved

Similar to Activity 1, plus the ability to place felt in correct position in the 'loft'

Unfamiliar words

Insulated, insulation, escapes

Safety points

1. See 'Safety points' for Activity 1.
2. Fibre glass should not be used since this may cause skin irritation.

General notes

1. See 'General notes' for Activity 1.
2. Since the questions on page 7 of the pupils' book require comparisons to be made between the results of Activity 1 and those of Activity 2, some help may be needed.
3. It is important to tell pupils that felt is not generally used for loft insulation; other materials such as fibre glass are used, but felt is more convenient to use for the investigation.

Apparatus list

2 thermometers
Beaker (600 cm³)
Sheet of cardboard to cover top of beaker
Stop clock
Polystyrene tile
Rubber bands
Plasticine
Felt underlay (approx 50 × 10 cm)
Felt pens (1 red and 1 green)
Scissors (if felt and cardboard are not cut to size)

Details for any construction
None

Activity 3:
Will air space stop heat from moving?

Objective
To carry out instructions and to make an attempt at interpreting the results

Experience
To investigate the effects of double glazing on the prevention of heat loss using a simulation Activity with glass beakers

Skills involved
1. Ability to understand written instructions
2. Transferring boiling water, e.g. from kettle to beakers
3. Reading thermometers accurately
4. Entering results correctly on the matrix table
5. Filling in the graph
6. Interpreting the graph

Unfamiliar words
Thermometer, zero, temperature, layer, trapped

Safety points
Care must be taken in securing the thermometers and in transferring the boiling water.

General notes
1. The main difficulty will be taking three readings of the thermometers at the same time.
2. Help may be needed with the construction of the graph and its interpretation.

Apparatus list
3 thermometers
3 beakers (150 cm³ tall form)
2 beakers (400 cm³ squat form)
Large polystyrene disc to cover large beaker
2 medium polystyrene discs to cover small beakers
3 small polystyrene discs to go underneath the small beakers
Plasticine
3 felt pens (1 red, 1 blue, 1 green)
Stop clock

Details for any construction
The discs needed to cover or stand the beakers on can be cut from a polystyrene tile using a hot wire cutter (these can be bought from most DIY stores). Alternatively a low voltage supply (6 V d.c.) and No 26 nichrome wire can be used. Cutting the tile with a knife is not very satisfactory.

Activity 4:
Which tiles wear best?

Objective
To systematically carry out a series of investigations related to a set of given criteria

Experience
Moving a house brick to and fro across various tile surfaces to investigate wear and tear

Skills involved
1. Setting up the Activity according to instructions
2. Recognising wear
3. Understanding the procedure for entering results

Unfamiliar words
Base, backwards, forwards, signs, score, wearing

Safety points
1. It is advisable to secure the base and tile with the G-clamp.
2. Place the base away from the edge of table to avoid the danger of the brick falling onto pupils' feet.

General notes
1. It is important that pupils understand that the number (50) of backward and forward movements of the brick must be the same for each tile being investigated.
2. Parts of these worn tiles will be needed for the Activities which follow.

Apparatus list
Several different varieties of floor tiles (these can be cut in half for reasons of economy)
Wooden base

House brick
String
Scissors
G-clamp

Details for any construction
The wooden base can be any piece of wood measuring approximately 30 cm × 30 cm.

Activity 5:
Do the tiles stain?

Objective
To systematically carry out a series of investigations related to a set of given criteria

Experience
Using a variety of household liquids on different floor tiles to find out if any permanent damage is done

Skills involved
1. Correct use of syringe for dropping liquids onto tiles
2. Ability to estimate the degrees of staining
3. Ability to award marks depending on the tile's resistance to staining (including both new and worn tiles)

Unfamiliar words
Worn, syringe, staining, resistance, permanent

Safety points
Syringes must be used correctly.

General notes
This Activity could be extended by using other household cleaning powders and liquids to try to remove stains. Again, is there any permanent damage caused by using these cleaning agents?

Apparatus list
A collection of small pieces (approx 3 cm²) of new and worn tiles (from Activity 4)
Household liquids, e.g. ink, gravy, blackcurrant juice, coffee, tea, food dyes, coloured jams
Small plastic syringe (or dropping tube)

Details for any construction
None

Activity 6:
Are the floor tiles affected by household bleach?

Objective
To systematically carry out a series of investigations related to a set of given criteria

Experience
To observe the effect of household bleach on floor tiles

Skills involved
1. Putting *equal* amounts of bleach onto each of the floor tiles
2. Recognising the effect, if any, on the different floor tiles

Unfamiliar words
Household, bleach, damage, purposes

Safety points
1. Care must be taken when handling bleach; if there should be contact with the skin, wash off immediately with cold water.
2. The cloth used for wiping the tile should be washed frequently. It is advisable to use plastic gloves for this purpose.

General notes
It is important that pupils should be told to use the bleach carefully.

Apparatus list
Selection of small pieces of floor tiles
Household bleach
Syringe
Wet cloth
Small beaker

Details for any construction
None

Activity 7:
How slippery are floor tiles?

Objective
To systematically carry out a series of investigations related to a set of given criteria

Experience
That some tiles under certain conditions are more slippery than others

Skills involved
1. Fixing a floor tile to the tilt apparatus
2. Controlled lifting of the tilt board
3. Measuring the height of the board
4. Using a matrix table to enter the results

Unfamiliar words
Height, measuring, important

Safety points
None

General notes
1. Since pupils have three tables of results to fill in, some guidance may be needed.
2. Before the pupils begin this Activity, a discussion on how to measure the height of the tilt board may be necessary, i.e. which edge of the board should be used to take readings.

Apparatus list
Selection of floor tiles (two sets are required, one dry and one wet)
Tilt measuring board
Rubber shoe sole fixed to 1 kg mass
Large clip (to secure tile to board)

Details for any construction
See diagram 29, page 150, for construction of the tilt measuring board.

Activity 8:
Do the tiles scorch or burn?

Objective
To systematically carry out a series of investigations related to a set of given criteria

Experience
Some tiles are more easily damaged by heat than others

Skills involved
1. Using matches correctly (i.e. safety-wise) to find out if a tile will burn

2. Recognising the degree of damage caused by the heat

Unfamiliar words
Heat resistant, depending, damaged, permanent

Safety points
1. Lighted matches should be used sensibly.
2. Fumes from burning tiles must not be inhaled.
3. For this experiment only small pieces of tile should be used.
4. Ensure that a satisfactory heat resistant mat is used.

General notes
1. It is important that pupils do not hold the tile pieces in their hands.
2. The damage caused by the dropping of lighted cigarettes onto floors could be discussed.

Apparatus list
Selection of tile pieces (only small pieces needed)
Box of matches
Heat resistant mats

Details for any construction
None

Activity 9:
Do the tiles dent?

Objective
To systematically carry out a series of investigations related to a set of given criteria

Experience
Some tiles can be damaged if heavy objects fall on them, particularly if these objects have sharp edges

Skills involved
1. Setting up the apparatus
2. Estimating the degree of damage to the tile
3. Using a magnifying glass to assist in finding the amount of penetration of the centre punch

Unfamiliar words
Centre punch, magnifying, pointed, several

Safety points
None

General notes
Some discussion will be needed to help pupils estimate the degree of damage to the tile since this will be relatively small.

Apparatus list
Selection of floor tiles (small pieces only)
90 cm length of tubing
Stand and clamp
Centre punch
Magnifying glass
Ruler

Details for any construction
Conduit tubing, as used in electrical wiring, is ideal for the 90 cm length of tubing. Make sure that the centre punch will fit inside the tube.

Activity 10:
Class results of tests

Objective
To gather and collate results from a series of investigations in order to produce a collective 'report'

Experience
Collecting and collating data to find out if any particular tile is better than others which have been tested

Skills involved
1. Finding averages
2. Making decisions from sets of results, depending on certain criteria

Unfamiliar words
None

Safety points
None

General notes
Some pupils when confronted with a collection of data may find difficulty arranging it in correct order. Some help may be needed here if pupils are to obtain maximum success from their efforts.

Apparatus list
None

Details for any construction
None

Activity 11:
Are detergents better than soap?

Objective
To investigate the effectiveness of some detergents

Experience
To investigate the effects of soap and detergent on different kinds of hard and soft waters

Skills involved
1. Correctly measuring the amount of water to be used for each test
2. Measuring and recording the number of times the syringe was filled with soap and detergent solution
3. Recognising the 'terminal' point, i.e. when suds remain for half a minute

Unfamiliar words
Detergent, syringe, 1 cm³, measuring cylinder, suds, produce, disadvantage

Safety points
None

General notes
1. Before pupils begin this Activity, some general discussion is needed.
2. Some skills may need revising, e.g. the correct method of measuring liquids.
3. It is important to impress upon the pupils that this type of Activity cannot be rushed.

Apparatus list
Soap solution (best made from liquid soft soap)
Liquid detergent solution
Water from a soft water district (or prepared in the laboratory)
Water from a hard water district (or prepared in the laboratory)
1 cm³ syringe
Measuring cylinder (50 cm³)

Details for any construction
None

Activity 12:
Making bath salts

Objective
To make simple household toiletries from a given chemical 'recipe'

Experience
A simple way of making bath salts

Skills involved
Adding only sufficient colouring to conform with the shade required

Unfamiliar words
Crystals, colouring

Safety points
None

General notes
A place must be reserved for crystals to be left to dry.

Apparatus list
Sodium sesquicarbonate crystals
Colouring (food dyes can be used)
Dropping tube
Clean test tubes in rack
Clean dish
Glass rod

Details for any construction
None

Activity 13:
The effect of bath salts on hard water

Objective
Ability to carry out an investigation that will test the effectiveness of specific products

Experience
Bath crystals can be used to soften water for washing purposes

Skills involved
1. Measuring specified amounts of hard water and transferring this to a flask
2. Measuring and recording the amount of soap solution used to obtain a permanent lather

Unfamiliar words
Reason, necessary, perfume

Safety points
None

General notes
See 'General notes' for Activity 11.

Apparatus list
Soap solution
Hard water
1 cm³ syringe
Measuring cylinder (50 cm³)
Sodium sesquicarbonate crystals (or bath salts)
Conical flask

Details for any construction
None

Activity 14:
The effect of enzymes on protein

Objective
Awareness of the action of enzymes on protein

Experience
To show that enzymes can 'digest' proteins under certain conditions

Skills involved
1. Setting up the Activity using 4 beakers
2. Putting into each beaker the correct constituents
3. Using a syringe to measure correct amounts of a liquid
4. Recognising changes that may take place

Unfamiliar words
Enzymes, protein, hydrochloric acid, pepsin, spatula, digest

Safety points
None

General notes
1. Class discussion will be needed before the pupils attempt this Activity.
2. The term 'biological detergents' will need explanation and so will 'protein', 'enzyme' and 'digest'.
3. A display of empty cartons of all kinds of washing powders and detergents may be a useful focus for discussion.

Apparatus list
Small pieces of white from hard boiled eggs
4 beakers (50 cm³ or 100 cm³)
Bottle of *dilute* hydrochloric acid
1 cm³ syringe
Pepsin powder — an enzyme
Small spatula or plastic spoon

Details for any construction
None

Activity 15:
The effect of different detergents on protein

Objective
Awareness that enzymes are used in some detergent powders

Experience
To find the effects of different kinds of detergent (enzyme and non-enzyme) on protein

Skills involved
1. Setting up and labelling beakers
2. Measuring stated amounts of detergent into each beaker
3. Collecting and collating results

Unfamiliar words
Non-enzyme, addition, 'control', biological, digest

Safety points
None

General notes
1. Quite a number of beakers will be needed for this Activity.
2. Make sure that labelling has been done correctly and that each group can identify its set of beakers.
3. A warm place is also needed.
4. Discussion on the end results is necessary before questions are attempted.

Apparatus list
A number of small beakers (50 cm³ or 100 cm³)
The white from hard-boiled eggs
Different detergents (enzyme and non-enzyme)
Spatula or plastic teaspoon
Self-adhesive labels or chinagraph pencil

Details for any construction
None

Activity 16:
Staining cloths with different protein stains

Objective
Ability to recognise substances which will produce a protein stain

Experience
Preparation of stained material to be used in future tests

Skills involved
1. Preparation of stain

2. Applying stain to materials provided
3. Correct labelling of the stained material

Unfamiliar words
Substances, egg yolk, stain

Safety points
None

General notes
It is important that labelling has been done correctly so that stains can be identified when dry.

Apparatus list
A large number of pieces of white cotton material (approx 5 cm × 5 cm)
Syringe (1 cm³)
Various substances for staining, e.g. egg yolk, milk, gravy, tea, coffee, cocoa, fruit juices, tomato sauce

Details for any construction
None

Activity 17:
The effect of biological detergents on different stains

Objective
To test the effectiveness of some biological detergents on stained material

Experience
That some detergents are better at removing protein stains than others

Skills involved
1. Arranging and labelling correctly the beakers to be used for the test
2. Adding the *same* amount of detergent to each beaker
3. Using and reading a thermometer
4. Being able to recognise differences

Unfamiliar words
Thermometer, luke-warm, rinse, compare, completely

Safety points
Care is needed in heating the water and detergent to 60°C.

General notes
1. Some form of collecting and collating a class result will be needed.
2. Discussion is needed before pupils attempt to answer questions.

Apparatus list
None

Details for any construction
None

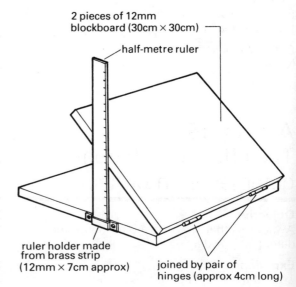

2 pieces of 12mm blockboard (30cm × 30cm)
half-metre ruler
ruler holder made from brass strip (12mm × 7cm approx)
joined by pair of hinges (approx 4cm long)

DIAGRAM 29. Construction of tilt measuring board (Activity 7).

Answers to questions in pupils' book

A letter D indicates that the answer cannot be predicted, usually because it is dependent on the results of the class experiments.

Activity 1
1(a),(b), 2. D
3. Yes
4. Through the cardboard
5. By insulating the floor of the loft

Activity 2
1. (a) Red
  (b) Green
2. From the room below
3. When it is not used
4. No. They do not lose their heat to the loft so easily.
5. Insulate the loft.
6. No. The house would stay warmer because the heat would not escape and less heat would have to be replaced.

Activity 3
1. Red
2. Green
3. Only the inner beaker is covered in the blue set; both beakers are covered in the green set.
4. No
5. Red
6. Green
7. The warm air between the walls of the beakers could not escape.
8. Add an extra sheet of glass or plastic to provide an air pocket between the room and the outside.
9. Green
10. Heat loss would decrease so less money would be spent on heating.

Activity 4
1. By pulling a brick across the different tiles the same number of times
2. Yes
3. Using the hand might cause the pressure used to vary. Pulling with string makes the pressure easier to control.
4. D

Activity 5
1. Yes
2. The rough surface traps the stain.

Activity 6
1. Many tiles will be affected but a good quality tile may not.
2. To clean and disinfect

Activity 7
1. Wax the tiles and then test them as before.
2. The one that shows the most slippery condition since this would be the most dangerous.
3. People can have or can cause serious accidents when they slip.

Activity 8
1. Try cleaning it.

Activity 9
1. (a) So the punch drops vertically down with its point first.
  (b) So it is dropped from the same height each time.
  (c) If it was much longer it would be more difficult to handle.

Activity 10
1, 2. D

Activity 11
1. More soap is needed to make suds.
2. D
3. Yes. Because it lathers better in water than soap does.
4. They may be used in automatic washing machines. They make clothes softer.
5. It would be bad for your skin if you used it that often.

Activity 13
1. In the hard water only
2. Soften it
3. To make the water softer
4. No
5. To make the salts look and smell nicer

Activity 14
1. D
2. Pepsin and acid
3. Protein acid
4. Blood, egg, milk, curry, gravy
5. Detergent with enzymes — biological detergents

Activity 15
1-3. D
4. As a control. If the egg white were 'digested' by the water, the detergents would not be needed.

Activity 17
1-3. D

Snaps and Circuits

Summary of contents

This Unit has two distinct sections, one dealing with simple electronic circuits and the other with simple photography. Both sections are practical in nature and therefore introduce many new skills.

Electronics (circuits)

The first two Activities are designed to allow the pupils the opportunity of learning the skills necessary to hold and use an electric soldering iron. The making of simple electronic circuits follows, starting with the construction of a diode receiver. The pupils are then encouraged to use their skills further by making circuit boards, amplifiers, flip-flop circuits and a light operated switch. These have been included not so much as an introduction to a course on electronics but as exercises in providing experiences in the use of basic electronic components, such as diodes, transistors, capacitors and resistors.

Photography (snaps)

The main objective of this part of the Unit is to stimulate an interest in photography as a worthwhile hobby. The basic scientific principles underlying photography are introduced, but the materials have been kept fairly simple and all the suggested Activities can be carried out using standard laboratory black-out conditions. First, detailed instructions are given on how to *make* light sensitive paper. (Included in this book are instructions on how to make and use blueprint paper.) This is followed by an Activity which *uses* the paper to produce a photogram or photograph without the use of a camera. These exercises provide the pupil with experience in handling and processing sensitised material. Details of how to construct a simple pin-hole camera are outlined. This leads on to the use of a camera and an awareness of how film is used to record a permanent negative image by developing and fixing the film. There are further suggested Activities in 'Notes for teacher', page 160 on how this interest can be extended.

Equipment list for Electronics section

To be made
None

To be bought or obtained from other departments
Soldering irons
Solder
A small amount of wood for bases
Copper board
Nail varnish
Nail varnish remover
9 V batteries
6 V lamps, M.E.S. (4)
Lampholders, M.E.S. (4)
Diode, type not important (1)
1N 4001 diodes (2)
1N 4148 diode (1)
BC 108 transistors (6)
2N 3053 transistor (1)
100 μF capacitors (5)
500 pF capacitors (2)
0.1 μF capacitors (3)
300 pF capacitor (1)
22K resistors (2)
2K2 resistor (1)
4K7 resistors (3)
470 Ω resistor (1)
10K resistor (1)
1K resistors (2)
3K3 resistor (1)
150 Ω resistor (1)
1K5 resistor (1)
Light sensitive resistor, ORP 12 (1)
5K variable resistor (1)

Loudspeaker, RS 3 $3/8''$, 35 Ω (1)
Ferrite rod (1)
Relay, 9 V (1)
Headphones or earphones (1)
Note: The numbers in brackets are the quantities needed to make *one* of each of the models.

Many electronics parts can be obtained from R.S. Components Ltd, P.O. Box 427, 13-17 Epworth Street, London EC2P 2HA, telephone 01-253 3040. There are also branches for the Midlands and the North-West.

To be collected
Cardboard tubes

Assumed normally available in laboratory
Bare copper wire (S.W.G. 18, 20)
Wire cutters
Insulated copper wire (S.W.G. 26)
1'' nails
4'' nails
Heat resistant mats
Hand drill
Several small drills (1/16'')
Cotton wool
Iron III chloride
Shallow dishes
Plastic gloves
Plastic tongs
Plastic covered wire (extra flexible RC)
P.V.C. tape
Ray box

Equipment list for Photography section

To be made
Printing frames (Activities 11, 13, 14 and 15)
Light tight box for keeping sensitive paper (Activity 12)
Exposing light on stand (optional, Activity 15)
Smoke box (Activity 17)

To be bought or obtained from other departments
Bulldog clips

Aluminium foil (kitchen foil)
Photographic dishes
Plastic tongs
Single glide track (as used for cupboard doors)
Sheets of hardboard
Sheets of clear, rigid plastic
Contact paper
Projection paper
Bromide enlarging paper
Cutting knife or safety type razor blade
Coloured transparent plastic sheet (e.g. red and green)
Plasticine
12 mm plywood for making boxes and stands

To be collected
Newspapers
Typing copy paper (carbon paper)
Blotting paper
Several items for making silhouette prints
Black and white negatives
Various sizes of cardboard tubes
Greaseproof paper
Brown paper
Tin lids

Assumed normally available in laboratory
Scissors
Sodium chloride
Silver nitrate
Glacial acetic acid
Beakers
Plastic gloves
Distilled water
Measuring cylinder
Balance
Rulers
Sodium thiosulphate
Stop clock or stop watch
P.V.C. tape
Rubber bands
Sewing needles
Clear light bulb in holder
Magnifying glass
Thick and thin card
Adhesive
Slide/strip projector
Convex lenses

Forward planner

Activity number	Advanced planning needed	Approximate Activity time (40 min period)	Are results of a previous Activity necessary?
1 and 2	Ensure that soldering irons are working, clean and safe to use	2-3 periods	No
3	Cut wooden boards to size. Collect small cardboard tubes (e.g. Smartie tubes). Test all diodes. Erect aerial and ensure that a good earth connection is handy	3 periods	No
4	Cut copper board to size (not less than 12 cm × 6 cm). Obtain small paint brushes for nail varnish. Make up iron III chloride solution	1 period	No
5	Useful if a 'booster' could be displayed. Ensure that all components are at hand in labelled boxes or trays	3 periods	Activity 4 (circuit board)
6	Useful if a completed model could be displayed. Use P.V.C. tape not sellotape. Cut boards to size (as for Activity 4)	3 periods	No
7	Cut boards to size. Use good quality carbon paper. Check that you have sufficient iron III chloride solution	3 periods	No
8	Cut boards to size. It may be preferable to bend the capacitor lugs yourself	3 periods	No
9	Cut boards to size (12 cm × 9 cm). Solder wires to relays, including thick bare wires. Check to see that they are functioning properly before allowing pupils to use them	3 periods	No
10	Arrange suitable stance for electromagnet. Try out electromagnet for optimum length of coil	2-3 periods depending on sustained interest	Activity 9 (light operated switch
11	Make plenty of printing frames	1 period	No
12	If pupils will not be allowed to make up their own solutions, adequate stock solutions should be available. Make light tight box	2 periods	No
13	Have available plenty of items for printing	1 period	Activity 12 (light sensitive paper)

Forward planner

Activity number	Advanced planning needed	Approximate Activity time (40 min period)	Are results of a previous Activity necessary?
14	Some exposed 'prints' could be prepared	1-2 periods	Activity 12 (light sensitive paper). Could use some 'prints' from Activity 13
15	Collect a selection of black and white negatives. Some extra sheets of sensitive paper should be available. Make exposing light (optional)	2-3 periods	Activity 12 (light sensitive paper) and Activity 14 (fixed 'negative' image)
16	It may be wise to collect an assortment of cardboard tubes. Then card and P.V.C. tape should be available if pupils wish to make their own tubes.	3 periods	No
17	Make smoke box. Need a good supply of cardboard cut to size to fit in front of smoke box	1 period	Activity 16

Notes for teacher — Electronics section

It is recommended that each circuit in this section is made and tested by the teacher before the relevant lesson.

Activity 3

Possible failure of the crystal set may be due to any of the following:

1. A faulty diode. This can be tested using an avometer as follows: Switch the avometer to 'ohms'. Place the meter probes across the diode and note the reading. Remove the probes, reverse them and place them across the diode again. In one instance you should obtain a very low resistance reading (forward resistance), and in the other, a very high resistance. If this is not the case, try another diode.

2. Poor aerial or earth (the latter being equally as important as the aerial). Do not trust water pipes as they may have plastic jointing. Try to get your aerial *outside*. It should be at least 16 m long and as high as possible.

3. An incorrectly wound coil. The turns should be side by side (not pile wound).

The aerial, or antenna, collects small voltages of differing high frequencies (radio frequencies) and transfers this radio frequency energy to the tuned circuit.

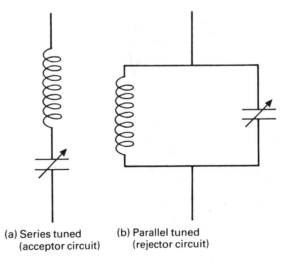

(a) Series tuned (acceptor circuit)

(b) Parallel tuned (rejector circuit)

DIAGRAM 30. Series and parallel tuned circuits.

A capacitor and a coil (inductance) connected either in series, diagram 30 (a), or in parallel, diagram 30 (b), constitute a tuned circuit, which will either accept or reject a particular frequency.

In the receiver then, the circuit is parallel tuned and rejects a particular frequency, which is then passed to the diode. All other frequencies are accepted and pass to earth.

A radio wave is a high frequency carrier wave modulated by an audio frequency.

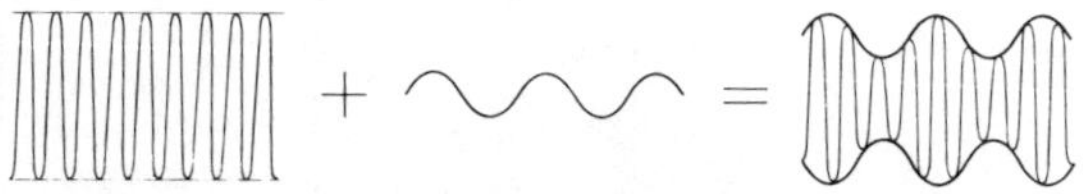

high frequency   audio frequency   modulated
carrier wave   carrier wave

DIAGRAM 31. A radio wave.

The function of the diode is to partly rectify this signal, extracting from it the audio frequencies only and passing this low frequency voltage to the earphones.

The frequency rejected depends upon two factors — the value of the inductance and that of the capacitance. It is determined by the relationship

$$f = \frac{1}{2\pi \sqrt{LC}}$$

where
L = Inductance of coil in henry
C = Capacitance in farad
f = Frequency rejected in hertz (cycles/s)

Although signals will be heard, the receiver suffers inherently from the following disadvantages, which cannot be overcome to any appreciable extent.
1. Lack of sensitivity — there is no stage of amplification.
2. Lack of selectivity — more than one station may be tuned simultaneously.

Note: The earth is as important as the antenna in the above device. **Do not use mains earth.**

Pupils may wish to try their luck using a piece of coke (about the size of a pea) instead of the diode. This must be somehow fixed in place and 'tickled' with the wires.

In theory *any* diode will work, provided it has a good front-to-back ratio, i.e. a very high resistance in one direction and a very low resistance in the other direction.

Activity 4
The procedure for making the printed circuit board is given in the pupils' book, but the following notes may be useful.
1. After the board has been cut, it should be cleaned with wire wool or Brasso.
2. Shellac in ethyl ethanoate can be used as an alternative to nail varnish, or any fast drying waterproof paint (e.g. car touch-up paint). Other possible alternatives include strips of waterproof insulating tape and special etch resistant pens.
3. The varnish (or paint or ink) must be allowed to dry thoroughly.
4. The iron III chloride solution should be almost saturated (very dark brown). It works best at 60-70°C.
5. When all traces of copper have disappeared, the board must be washed thoroughly in cold water. Any iron III chloride solution left behind will continue to etch. The nail varnish, etc., should then be removed by a suitable solvent.
6. For a professional appearance the board can be sprayed, even before soldering, with Printed Circuit Lacquer.

Activity 5
When making up the printed circuit board, care must be taken with the following.
1. All capacitors must be wired in observing the correct polarity.
2. Resistors should be connected in their correct positions in the circuit. It does not matter if they do not lie flat. The resistor colour code (see page 3 of pupils' book) should be explained to pupils. The group of three coloured bands indicates the value of

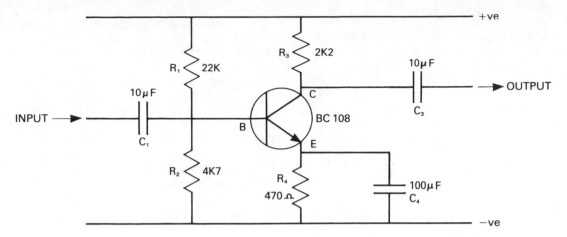

DIAGRAM 32. Circuit for a one-transistor amplifier.

the resistor and the fourth band indicates its tolerance (usually 20%).

If any of the resistors in the circuit get hot there is probably a wiring error and the circuit should be checked.

3. The transistor should be left until last. Ensure that the base, collector and emitter are soldered in at the right places as shown. If the amplifier fails to function check for any 'dry joints'. These will appear greyish and dull instead of bright and shiny. They constitute a high resistance where there should be no resistance at all. If they are seen, simply remelt the existing solder, keeping the components quite still while the solder sets hard.

4. Crocodile clips should be used to connect the amplifier to the crystal set.

5. Make sure that the battery is connected the right way round. This is most important.

Diagram 32 shows a standard circuit diagram of a one-transistor amplifier.

R_1 and R_2 constitute a potential divider. C_1 being a capacitor will prevent the passage of d.c. through it and so to the microphone, but will allow audio frequency a.c. to pass through it from the microphone to the base of the BC 108. R_3 ensures that the correct d.c. voltage is applied at the collector (see manufacturer's details if interested) and R_4

prevents too much current from entering the transistor and making it hot. C_3 performs the same function as C_1 and allows the passage of amplified audio through it, but prevents a.c. from the supply (via R_3) from reaching the next stage.

The next stage may be a duplicate of the above or it may be, as in our case, earphones.

A small change in current at the base (B) causes a larger change in current at the collector. This is true of any transistor connected as an amplifier.

Activities 6 and 7
The only snag likely to be encountered in making the slow flip-flop (Activity 6) is short circuiting. Before the power is applied it is therefore essential to check that wires do not touch each other where they are not supposed to. Also make sure that the transistors are connected correctly — making the connections can be awkward and the three leads may easily touch each other if care is not taken. The timing of the device is governed by the capacitors and resistors — the more adventurous pupils may like to alter the values of these to see what effect this has on timing.

There should be no difficulty in making the fast flip-flop (Activity 7), apart from the time it takes! To cut down the etching time, 50/50 nitric acid could be used instead of iron III

157

chloride solution. However, nitric acid and its fumes can be dangerous, so great care must be taken. When making up the circuit, make sure that the wire bridging the sloping track has insulation on it (as shown in the diagram on page 13 of the pupils' book).

The circuit diagram for the fast flip-flop is shown below. The slow flip-flop circuit is essentially the same as this and works in the same way. The only difference is that the slow flip-flop has two bulbs replacing the two 1K resistors and two diodes connected to each of the two transistor base leads.

In the circuit below each transistor acts as a switch. When an emf is applied, a pulse of current passes through T_1 and on to T_2, producing a click in the speaker. But part of this current can return to T_1 via capacitor C_1. This allows a second pulse to pass over the same path and the action is repeated. The energy to the speaker is continuous since the pulses are amplified as they are applied to the transistor bases. The intervals between the pulses may be altered by varying C_1 and C_2 or R_1 and R_2. Very slow pulses may be obtained by making C_1/C_2 very large, say 1000 or more. The flip-flop then becomes a metronome or timer.

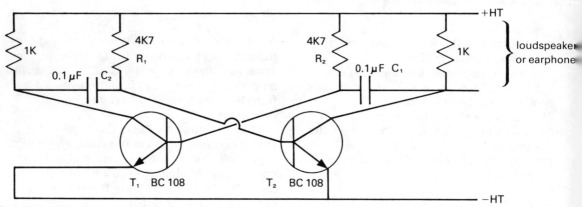

DIAGRAM 33. Circuit for a fast flip-flop.

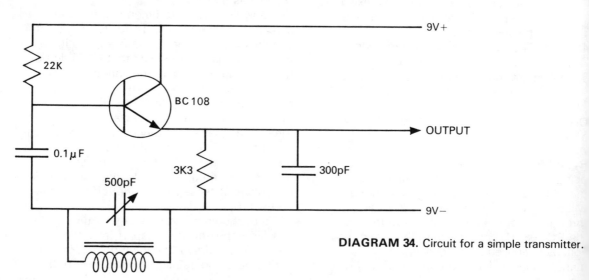

DIAGRAM 34. Circuit for a simple transmitter.

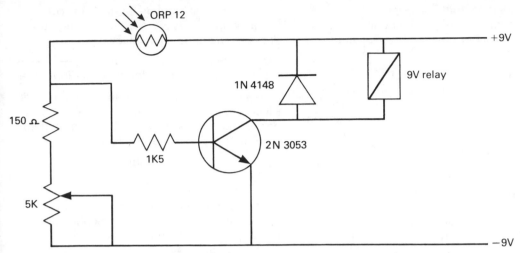

DIAGRAM 35. Circuit for a light sensitive switch.

Activity 8

Facing is a circuit diagram for the simple transmitter.

Little difficulty is experienced in building up the board, although it is recommended, as in all cases, that a trial circuit is made up and tested by the teacher beforehand.

If no signals can be found on the medium wave, then connect a 100 pF capacitor in series with the aerial lead, and connect this to an oscilloscope to check that a radio frequency is being produced. It undoubtedly will be, but with such a simple circuit it is difficult to guarantee the frequency. If the oscilloscope test proves that radio frequency is present, experimenting with the number of turns on the coil will eventually bring out the frequency to the medium wave band.

The iron III chloride solution for etching the copper must be strong and warm, otherwise it will take a long time to work.

Activities 9 and 10

The resistance of the CdS cell is reduced as the light falling on it increases. Hence under no-light conditions, the resistance is at a maximum and the transistor is cut off. The 5K sensitivity control helps combat ambient light conditions. Ideally a slightly darkened room will enhance the efficiency of the device.

It is essential that the diode is connected

the right way round as this prevents back emf from the relay damaging the transistor. Other transistors (e.g. BFY 50, BFY 51) will work with varying degrees of sensitivity. Even the BC 108 will work in this circuit.

The board could be made much smaller than 12 × 9 cm, i.e. 4 × 2.5 cm, but then wiring and etching become rather tedious.

Although crude, the ball bearing (Activity 10) has a nerve shattering effect if allowed to drop onto the right things!

Notes for teacher — Photography section

It is hoped that this section will give pupils an understanding of the basic scientific principles underlying photography, while at the same time stimulating interest in photography as a hobby.

The materials have been kept fairly simple and for this work no great stress has been put upon the need for a darkroom. It is hoped that an ordinary laboratory black-out will suffice. Schools which have a darkroom and extra equipment such as enlargers will be able to take the Activities further.

Some additional material is included in these notes (rather than in the pupils' books) to allow the teacher flexibility in planning the course.

Activity 11

One method of introducing this Activity is to ask the pupils to look around for examples where light has caused a change in colour and where living things have reacted to light. The following points could be discussed.

1. What happens when our skin is exposed to sunlight? (This could include consideration of skin pigmentation and protection against sunburn.)
2. What effect does light have on plants? (Photosynthesis and phototropism.)
3. Why do fabrics, e.g. curtains, fade?
4. Why do some shops cover their windows with sheets of transparent yellow material? Do other colours have the same effect?
5. What effect does light have on newsprint? (Activity 11 provides the answer.)

Activity 12

To introduce pupils to the idea that some chemicals are sensitive to light, the teacher could carry out the following demonstration experiment. In two separate test tubes mix equal volumes of silver nitrate and sodium chloride solutions. A white precipitate will form. Put one tube in the dark and expose the other to sunlight. The latter should darken noticeably, while the one in darkness remains unchanged. This shows that the colour change was caused by sunlight.

In making the light sensitive paper teachers may wish to cut down the time involved by, for example, making up the two solutions or cutting and 'salting' the paper prior to the lesson. A laboratory oven or hairdryer will prove invaluable for the drying process.

The quantities of chemicals given in the pupils' book are sufficient to prepare approximately 50 pieces of light sensitive paper. The paper may be prepared without black-out but strong daylight or sunlight must be prevented from falling on the working area.

The chemical processes are not discussed in the pupils' book but teachers may wish to give an explanation to some pupils.

The chemical reaction carried out to produce light sensitive silver chloride in the fibres of the paper is as follows:

silver nitrate + sodium chloride $\longrightarrow$ silver chloride + sodium nitrate

When light falls on to the paper some of this silver chloride is converted to metallic silver, producing a black mark on the paper and so recording the action of the light:

silver chloride $\xrightarrow{\text{light}}$ silver (black)

Teachers may wish to incorporate some history of photography at this stage by introducing the work of J. Herschel (sodium thiosulphate fixer) and W.H. Fox Talbot (photographic drawings).

As a further optional Activity pupils could make and use blueprint paper. Here the action of light is to change a soluble complex of yellow ferric ferricyanide to an insoluble Prussian blue. This paper is simple to make and development and fixing are carried out by washing in running water until the unexposed portion turns from yellow to white, then soaking in very dilute hydrochloric acid (1% solution) and then washing again in running water.

Solutions required are:
potassium ferricyanide (10 g) in distilled water (100 cm³)
(green) ammonium ferric citrate (25 g) in distilled water (100 cm³)

Equal volumes are mixed in the darkroom or in subdued light and brushed onto duplicating paper. The paper is then dried and kept in the dark ready for use. The paper should be yellow and in daylight turns to a bronze-blue. The colour is intensified in the hydrochloric acid bath.

The two solutions are both quite stable separately but when mixed they will not keep.

Pupils can be asked to make a tracing and then expose it to daylight in contact with blueprint paper under a sheet of glass or in a printing frame, until the uncovered paper turns a deep colour. This exposed paper should then be developed and fixed as described above.

Activities 13-15

Making photograms or photographs without a camera gives the pupil experience of handling and processing sensitised materials.

It can be explained to pupils that it was discovered that long before the light sensitive material has darkened visibly (as in their experiments), the light falling on it has affected the particles of silver salts in such a way that they can be rapidly converted to silver by treatment with a suitable chemical solution, i.e. the developer. The unseen image is known as the latent (hidden) image.

For use in schools undertaking this work with groups of children in rooms where black-out is imperfect, the light sensitive paper known as P153 is recommended. It is a projection paper with a yellow base and is very contrasty. It is designed for line drawings not photographs, but is has been used in Nuffield schemes in schools because it gives good results in conditions totally unsuitable for conventional bromide papers.

Kodak P153 paper is processed in the conventional way but if the light in the darkened room is bright then the print in the development stage should be shaded. Schools with conventional darkrooms equipped with safelights and enlargers can produce photograms using bromide paper. Images produced in photograms without the use of the camera or enlarger require little skill but give great scope for creativity and enjoyment.

In Activity 13 photograms are made by placing objects on a piece of the sensitised paper form Activity 12. This is exposed to light and processed in the normal manner.

All kinds of objects may be used — leaves, feathers, paper clips, paper cut-outs, rice, protractors, keys, etc. The light for exposure can be a lamp in a holder held over the sensitised paper at a suitable distance or sunlight, depending on the weather and location of the building. The length of time required is the minimum necessary to produce a dense black after processing.

The Activity may also be tried with Kodak C145 paper, a slow contact printing paper produced mainly for schools. Again it may be used in darkened laboratory conditions, but it is only produced in one size (8.9 × 12.7 cm). After exposure the paper is developed for 2 min at 20°C, washed and fixed for the length of time stated for the fixer being used.

Activities 16 and 17

The main idea here is to show the pupil how the 'lens' in a camera produces an image. Emphasis on the definition of the image is important since the quality of a print or slide depends on this.

There should be few problems in making a simple pin-hole camera. However, if the teacher allows pupils to develop the idea further by providing them with the opportunity and resources to redesign the suggested pin-hole camera, better results could be obtained.

If a 126 instamatic cartridge is used and a sufficiently light tight 'camera' can be designed and modelled around the cartridge, an attempt can be made to expose a film.

If the idea is too ambitious the pupils should be allowed to use the standard instamatic 126 camera. Provided that black and white film is used, pupils should with a little practice be able to develop and fix the film using a developing tank. If a daylight loader is not available the technique of using a 'changing bag' is not too difficult. Obviously if darkroom facilities are available, these should be used.

Once some proficiency has been obtained and pupils' interest maintained, attempts could be made (a) to produce a photoplay, i.e. an exercise in making a series of pictures which tell a story, or (b) to use colour reversal film or black and white dia-direct film to make slides, and (c) if a tape recorder is available to attempt a form of tape synchronisation.

161

Main objectives and ideas for Electronics section

Main objectives

1. Development of basic skills in soldering
2. Ability to 'read' a drawing of a simple electronic circuit
3. A knowledge of some of the components used in electronic circuits
4. Awareness that electronic circuits are used in many ways, not just for radios
5. Awareness that radio waves are produced electronically

Key ideas

1. That a good soldered joint is most important in electronic circuits
2. That solder is a kind of 'glue' which conducts electricity
3. To produce a simple working model, using electronic components, from drawings and written instructions
4. To become familiar with electronic components and to be able to recognize simple ones
5. To make and use models which illustrate the meaning of 'automation'

Main objectives and ideas for Photography section

Main objectives

1. To stimulate an interest in the basic skills of photography
2. Ability to handle sensitised material including paper and film
3. To understand the function of the basic parts in a simple camera

Key ideas

1. To encourage pupils to handle photographic materials
2. To allow pupils to process exposed photographic paper and films
3. To consider a little of the history of photography
4. To teach the basic skills needed to handle simple cameras

Information for each Activity

Activity 1: Getting good at soldering

Objective
Ability to use an electric soldering iron

Experience
Using a soldering iron to join wires together

Skills involved

1. Ability to hold a soldering iron correctly
2. Ability to use a soldering iron correctly
3. To prepare and position wires before soldering

Unfamiliar words
Electric, circuits, soldering, electricity, flux

Safety points

1. It is best if 110/115 V soldering irons can be used, i.e. through an isolating transformer. If mains soldering irons are used, heat resistant sleeving must completely cover the mains cable to the iron.
2. Make sure that there is a safe place to put the soldering iron when it is not being used. Coiled metal springs can be purchased for this purpose.

General notes
It is important that pupils master the techniques of soldering before they attempt to wire circuits.

Apparatus list
Soldering irons
Solder with flux
Wire (copper — various thicknesses)
Emery cloth (fine)
Steel wool
A stand to rest the soldering iron on when not in use
Heat resistant mat

Details for any construction
None

Activity 2:
Soldering shapes

Objective
Appreciation that both tools and surfaces to be soldered must be perfectly clean if good 'joins' are to be obtained

Experience
Developing soldering techniques by constructing various two- and three-dimensional shapes using copper wire

Skills involved
1. Ability to solder three wires together at different angles
2. Ability to measure and cut the wire to be used for the specific shapes

Unfamiliar words
Diagrams, accurate

Safety points
Take normal precautions regarding the use of soldering irons (see Activity 1).

General notes
1. If enough soldering irons are available it is best to work in groups of two or three.
2. Demonstration will obviously be necessary here and direct help may need to be given to some pupils.

Apparatus list
Copper wire (bare; S.W.G. 22 is a useful size)
Wire cutters or pliers
Solder with flux
Soldering iron
Heat resistant mat
Small portable bench vices would be useful

Details for any construction
None

Activity 3:
Making a diode receiver

Objective
Ability to solder components together in order to construct a simple electronic circuit

Experience
Making a simple radio receiver

Skills involved
1. Ability to accurately copy a diagram
2. Ability to recognise a capacitor and a diode
3. Ability to construct a radio coil
4. Ability to solder the components in the correct order

Unfamiliar words
Diode, earphone, loudspeaker, insulated wire, 500 pF capacitor, aerial

Safety points
Take normal precautions regarding the use of soldering irons (see Activity 1).

General notes
1. Some discussion and briefing will be needed here:
   (a) drawing the diagram onto a piece of wood
   (b) putting the aerials in the correct place
   (c) winding the coil
   (d) tuning the circuit.
2. Make sure that it is possible to obtain a good earth and a good aerial.

Apparatus list
Wooden board (base for receiver)
Cardboard tube
Copper wire (e.g. 24 S.W.G.) bare
Copper wire (e.g. 26 S.W.G.) insulated
Diode
1" nails
500 pF variable capacitor
Headphones or earphones
Solder
Soldering iron
Heat resistant mat
Support for soldering iron

Details for any construction
None

Activity 4:
Making a printed circuit board

Objective
Knowledge of how to produce, chemically, a printed circuit board

Experience
Making a printed circuit board using chemicals

Skills involved
1. Ability to prepare a copper circuit board from a set of written instructions
2. Using a hand drill to make small holes in the copper board

Unfamiliar words
Components, loudness, booster, varnish, iron III chloride solution, dissolve

Safety points
Take normal precautions regarding the handling of chemicals.

General notes
The reasons for taking the various steps in the process of producing the circuit board and the simple chemistry of the reaction could be explained.

Apparatus list
Copper board
Nail varnish
Small drill (3/32")
Hand drill
Cotton wool
Nail varnish remover
Iron III chloride solution
Shallow dish

Details for any construction
None

Activity 5:
A loudness booster

Objective
Ability to recognise a transistor and an awareness of its use in an amplifying circuit

Experience
To construct a one transistor amplifier to boost the signal from the diode receiver

Skills involved
1. Ability to identify radio components
2. Ability to solder components onto the prepared circuit board as indicated on the diagram and having regard to the polarity of some components
3. Ability to check the progress of each stage of the construction
4. Ability to check values of resistors by using a colour code

Unfamiliar words
Transistor, resistor, components, input

Safety points
Take normal precautions regarding the use of soldering irons (see Activity 1).

General notes
1. It is important that pupils realise that the diagram of the transistor (page 9 of pupils' book) shows the positions of the wires from the *underside.*
2. Pupils may need considerable help with this Activity. It would be better if one *type* of component was soldered first, e.g. all the resistors then all the capacitors and then the transistor. Slow but careful progress should be aimed at.

Apparatus list
Printed circuit board (from Activity 4)
BC 108 transistor
Two 100 μF capacitors
100 μF capacitor
22K resistor
2K2 resistor
4K7 resistor
470 Ω resistor
Earphones
9 V battery
Connecting wires
Soldering iron
Solder

Details for any construction
None

Activity 6:
A slow flip-flop

Objective
Knowledge that a transistor can be used as a switch

Experiences
1. To prepare a circuit board by chemical means
2. To solder given components to a circuit board to produce a slow flip-flop

Skills involved
1. Ability to prepare and make a circuit board
2. To recognise components and to solder these onto the circuit board using step by step instructions

Unfamiliar words
Automatically, iron III chloride solution, insulated

Safety points
Take normal precautions regarding the handling of chemicals and the use of soldering irons (see Activity 1).

General notes
1. Careful preparation of the circuit board is essential.
2. It is important that pupils understand the meaning of polarity of capacitors.

Apparatus list
Copper board
Iron III chloride solution
Sticky tape (insulating tape)
Soldering iron
Solder
Two 10K resistors
Two 100 μF capacitors
Two BC 108 transistors
Two diodes (1N 4001)
Two 6 V lamps (M.E.S.)
Two lampholders (M.E.S.)
Connecting wire
9 V battery

Details for any construction
None

Activity 7:
A fast flip-flop

Objective
Awareness that switching on and off quickly by using a transistor will produce a 'musical' note

Experiences
1. To prepare a circuit board using the chemical method
2. To solder components to a prepared circuit board in order to produce a fast flip-flop

Skills involved
1. Preparation of circuit board
2. Ability to recognise the value of a resistor by the colour code method
3. Ability to check the completed circuit board with the original diagram

Unfamiliar words
Loudspeaker, components, morse key, insulated

Safety points
Take normal precautions regarding the handling of chemicals and the use of soldering irons (see Activity 1).

General notes
1. Check the prepared board before pupils attempt the soldering of components.
2. Avoid confusion by explaining that the circuit diagram at the top of page 13 (pupils' book) shows the transistor from the *top*, but the diagram at the side of the page shows the transistor from the *bottom*.

Apparatus list
Copper board
Carbon paper
Sharp pencil
Nail varnish
Nail varnish remover
Iron III chloride solution
Cotton wool
Small drill (1/16")
Two 1K resistors
Two 4K7 resistors
Two 0.1 μF capacitors
Two BC 108 transistors

9 V battery
Loudspeaker
Insulated wire

Details for any construction
None

Activity 8:
A simple transmitter

Objective
Ability to make from a diagram an electronic
model which will produce a radio frequency

Experience
1. To make a printed circuit board
2. To solder components to the board in order
   to produce a simple radio transmitter

Skills involved
1. Preparation of the circuit board
2. Making a solenoid by winding insulated
   wire onto a ferrite rod
3. Soldering components onto the board in
   the correct order according to instructions
4. Ability to check the finished model with the
   given drawing

Unfamiliar words
Ferrite rod, diagram, variable, insulation,
aerial, transmitter, produced

Safety points
Take normal precautions regarding the
handling of chemicals and the use of soldering
irons (see Activity 1).

General notes
1. Make sure that pupils understand the
   relevance of the two views of transistors
   (i.e. top and bottom view).
2. Winding of the coil must be carried out
   carefully in order to obtain a neat result.

Apparatus list
Copper board
Nail varnish
Nail varnish remover
Iron III chloride solution
Cotton wool
Small drill (1/16'')
Insulated wire

22K resistor
0.1 μF capacitor
3K3 resistor
300 pF capacitor
Transistor (BC 108)
500 pF variable capacitor
Ferrite rod

Details for any construction
None

Activity 9:
Light operated switch

Objective
Awareness that light can influence electrical
resistance when using a light sensitive resistor

Experiences
1. To prepare a circuit board
2. To solder given components to the board
   to produce a light operated switch

Skills involved
1. To prepare and make the circuit board
2. Ability to recognise the relay and the light
   sensitive resistor
3. Ability to solder actual components to the
   circuit board as shown in the circuit
   diagram

Unfamiliar words
Operated, sensitive, variable, relay

Safety points
Take normal precautions regarding the
handling of chemicals and the use of soldering
irons (see Activity 1).

General notes
1. There are three new components being
   used here: a relay, a light sensitive resistor
   and a variable resistor. It is important that
   pupils are made familiar with their
   functions.
2. Wires should be soldered onto relays
   before they are handed out to pupils (see
   diagram facing).

Apparatus list
Copper board

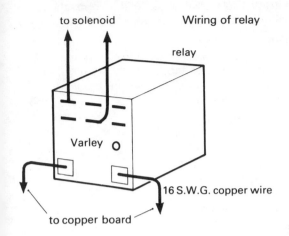

to solenoid   Wiring of relay

relay

Varley O

16 S.W.G. copper wire

to copper board

Nail varnish
Nail varnish remover
Iron III chloride solution
Cotton wool
Small drill (1/16")
Ray box
Soldering iron
Solder
Stand for soldering iron
Light sensitive resistor (ORP 12)
5K variable resistor
Transistor (2N 3053)
Relay with wires attached
Diode (1N 4148)
150 Ω resistor
1K5 resistor
Insulated wire

Details for any construction
Any two-pole changeover, 9 V relay can be
used. Before relays are given to pupils, wires
should be attached, as shown in the diagram
above.

Activity 10:
Using the light switch

Objective
Understanding the function of a relay in a
circuit and how it can be used to operate a
solenoid

Experience
Using a light sensitive switch circuit to operate
a simple electromagnet

Skills involved
1. Winding insulated wire onto a 4" nail to
   make an electromagnet
2. Setting up a complete circuit using the
   light sensitive switch in series with an
   electromagnet

Unfamiliar words
Electromagnet, ball bearing (steel ball)

Safety points
None

General notes
There is room to develop this Activity. If
possible allow pupils to design other models
using the light sensitive switch. Could a
simpler light source be constructed?

Apparatus list
Light operated switch (from Activity 9)
Insulated wire (S.W.G. 24 or 26)
Large nail (4")
Adhesive tape
Battery or low voltage power supply
Connecting wire (insulated)

Details for any construction
None

Activity 11:
The effect of light on newsprint

Objective
Awareness of the effect of prolonged
exposure to sunlight on certain materials

Experience
Finding the effect of sunlight on newspaper

Skills involved
1. To cut aluminium foil to a given shape and
   size
2. To cut out a 'shape' in the foil
3. To position the foil and newspaper in the
   correct order in the frame.

167

Unfamiliar words
Printing frame, aluminium foil, newspaper, sandwich, remove

Safety points
None

General notes
It might give added interest if groups investigated the effects of sunlight on a variety of different newspapers. Comparisons could then be made.

Apparatus list
Printing frame and clips or rubber bands
Aluminium foil
Razor blade (safety type) or scissors
Pieces of newspaper

Details for any construction
A simple printing frame can be made from squares of hardboard and *rigid* clear plastic held together with two rubber bands. Both hardboard and plastic should measure about 9 cm square.

Activity 12:
Making light sensitive paper

Objective
Knowledge of how to prepare chemical solutions

Experiences
1. To make up solutions of chemicals according to a set of instructions
2. To make light sensitive paper

Skills involved
1. Reading labels on bottles
2. Weighing out specific quantities of chemicals
3. Measuring specific volumes of liquids

Unfamiliar words
Sodium chloride, silver nitrate, glacial acetic acid, beaker, photographic dishes, distilled, semi-darkened, separate, dissolve, poisonous

Safety points
Extra care must be taken when handling silver nitrate and glacial acetic acid — both these chemicals can burn and stain the skin.

General notes
It may be considered desirable to prepare the solutions beforehand, as stock solution, and only allow the pupils to prepare the light sensitive papers.

Apparatus list
5 g sodium chloride*
10 g silver nitrate*
Glacial acetic acid*
Typing copy paper
Beakers*
Photographic dishes
Gloves or tongs
Blotting paper
Distilled water*
Measuring cylinder*
Balance*
Scissors
Ruler
Pencil
Light tight box for keeping sensitive paper

Note: Items marked with an asterisk are used to make the stock solutions. They will not be needed by pupils if the teacher prepares the solutions.

Details for any construction
The light sensitive paper has to be kept in a light tight box. This can be any metal box, such as an old biscuit tin, with a good fitting lid. Any seams should be sealed with P.V.C. insulating tape, and this should also be put round the rim of the lid to give an extra good fit. Alternatively, a bag can be made from black P.V.C. sheeting folded over and held with a bulldog clip.

Activity 13:
Using light sensitive paper

Objective
Knowledge that certain chemically treated papers possess a light sensitive property

Experience

Using the light sensitive paper made in Activity 12 to investigate what effect light has on the paper

Skills involved

Correctly positioning the light sensitive paper in relation to the 'object' and the printing frame

Unfamiliar words

Sensitised, protected, depend, brightness, darkening

Safety points

Pupils should wash their hands after handling the light sensitive paper.

General notes

The exposure times needed are quite long, about 10-15 minutes in bright light. Other similar group Activities should therefore be organised in conjunction with this Activity.

Apparatus list

Prepared pieces of light sensitive paper (from Activity 12)
Printing frame
Several objects suitable for printing

Details for any construction
See 'Details for any construction', Activity 11 for construction of the printing frame.

2. Recognising the correct exposure using a stop clock or stop watch
3. Carrying out the correct procedure for washing and drying the 'print'

Unfamiliar words

Sodium thiosulphate, photographic dish, balance, tongs

Safety points

Take normal precaution regarding the handling of chemicals.

General notes

It may be wise to prepare several exposed 'prints' before the lesson, owing to the time needed for exposure.

Apparatus list

Printing frame
Light sensitive paper
Shapes or cut-outs
Sodium thiosulphate
Photographic dish
Tongs (plastic or stainless steel)
Beakers
Balance
Measuring cylinder
Stop clock or stop watch
Blotting paper

Details for any construction
See 'Details for any construction', Activity 11 for construction of the printing frame.

Activity 14:
'Fixing' light sensitive paper

Objective

Knowledge that certain chemicals in solution, if used on light sensitive paper, will prevent any further action by light on that paper

Experience

Using photographic fixing solution on exposed light sensitive paper

Skills involved

1. Making up a solution of fixer (i.e. a solution of sodium thiosulphate).

Activity 15:
Making a positive print

Objective

Knowledge of the techniques required to produce photographic prints

Experiences

Making a 'positive' print
(a) from a 'negative' print (Activity 14)
(b) from black and white negatives

Skills involved

1. Correct positioning of sensitive paper and negative print in printing frame
2. Exposing print to sunlight correctly

Unfamiliar words

Negative, image, positive, modern, photography

Safety points

None

General notes

If pupils have been successful it may be worth developing the Activity further by allowing them to use a camera to produce their own negatives, leading eventually to making their own contact prints.

Apparatus list

Light sensitive paper (home made, and a
  quantity of 'contact' paper or enlarging
  paper cut to size)
Printing frame
Fixed images (from Activity 14)
Rubber bands
Sodium thiosulphate solution
Photographic dish
Plastic tongs
Some black and white negatives
Exposing light (optional)

Details for any construction
See 'Details for any construction', Activity 11 for construction of the printing frame.
  See diagram 36 on facing page for construction of the optional exposing light.

Activity 16:
The pin-hole camera

Objective

To investigate the behaviour of a pin-hole source of light

Experiences

1. To make a simple pin-hole camera
2. To use a pin-hole camera to produce an image

Skills involved

1. Ability to construct a pin-hole camera from a set of instructions
2. To assess the results of multiple pin-holes regarding image formation

Unfamiliar words

Camera, aluminium foil, tracing paper, magnifying glass, darkened, unshaded, blurred, enlarge, backwards, forwards

Safety points

None

General notes

Pupils could be encouraged to redesign the pin-hole camera and perhaps a competition between groups could be organised. See 'Notes for teacher' for suggestions.

Apparatus list

Cardboard tube
Aluminium foil
Adhesive tape
Rubber bands
Needle
Sheet of tracing (or greaseproof) paper
Razor blade (safety type)
Scissors
Unshaded clear light bulb in holder
Magnifying glass

Details for any construction
None

Activity 17:
Using a lens in the camera

Objective

Knowledge of how a camera lens improves the image definition in a camera

Experience

Using a smoke box to observe the behaviour of light rays through a lens

Skills involved

1. Cutting card and making a 2 mm diameter hole in the correct position that will enable light to enter the box
2. Making two further holes and covering each with a different coloured plastic film
3. Observing and recording the paths of the rays of light through the box

Unfamiliar words

Projector, convex lens, gelatin (plastic sheet), camera, exposure, collecting, smouldering, supported, beam, replace, differently, coloured, diagram, image

Safety points
1. Use only a small quantity of smouldering brown paper.
2. Warn pupils that although the projector has a fan to cool it, it does get very hot.

General notes
A good source of light is important for this Activity and the filter (coloured transparent plastic) should be of reasonable quality.

Apparatus list
Slide or filmstrip projector (light source only needed)
Smoke box
Plasticine
Suitable convex lens
Tin lid
Some paper — preferably brown
Strips of coloured gelatin or coloured transparent plastic (2 different colours)
Stiff cardboard
Scissors
Ruler and pencil

Details for any construction
See diagram 37, for construction of the smoke box.

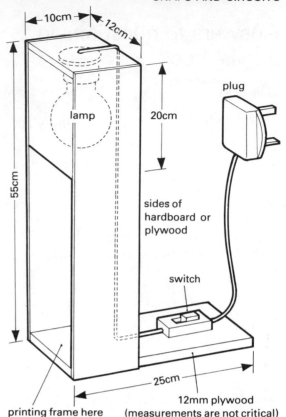

DIAGRAM 36. Construction of the exposing light and stand (Activity 15, optional).

DIAGRAM 37. Construction of the smoke box (Activity 17).

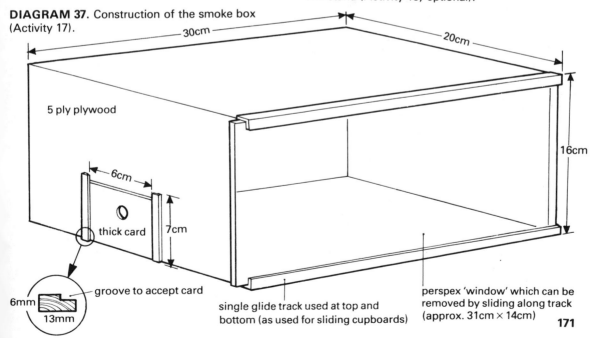

171

Answers to questions in pupils' book

A letter D indicates that the answer cannot be predicted, usually because it is dependent on the results of the class experiments.

Activity 11
1. D
2. The sunlight
3. Makes them fade

Activity 13
7. D
8. It goes dark all over.

Activity 14
5. It shouldn't.

Activity 15
5. Black and white are reversed.

6. It takes too long to react to the light.

Activity 16
What to do
5. It is upside down.
Should be sharp.
D.
It becomes larger and you can see less of it.
It becomes smaller.
6. Several
7. Blurred
Dim
10, 11. D

Questions
It gives a sharper, less blurred image.
Negative

Activity 17
6. Makes them more easily visible.
It has parallel sides.
Light beam is more concentrated, to a focal point.
9. Colours are the other way round.

Starting and Stopping

Summary of contents

Starting and Stopping considers the safety aspects when a motor vehicle is on the move. Speed and braking effects on various road surfaces are investigated. Further Activities consider why care should always be taken when driving round corners and the consequences that follow if precautions are not heeded. Activity 5 shows how differentials help cars round corners and Activity 6, for example, investigates whether front wheel skids are more dangerous than rear wheel skids.

In trying to identify the factors concerned with driving, it is hoped that pupils will be helped to lead safer lives both as pedestrians and as future drivers.

Some out of school Activities have also been included in order that first-hand information can be collected about traffic movement and traffic density. Although this information may have less personal significance for pupils, it may enable them to appreciate the Highway Authorities' problems and to take a more informed stance concerning future plans for new local roads.

Equipment list for whole of Unit

To be made

Skid test truck, meccano (Activities 1-4)
Wooden track with plastic guide rails
  (Activities 1-4)
Cart A and cart B, Fischer Technik (Activity 5)
Wooden board with plastic sheet (Activity 5)
Clip boards, for pupils' use outside school
  (Activities 7-11)

Forward planner

Activity number	Advanced planning needed	Approximate Activity time (40 min period)	Are results of a previous Activity necessary?
1	None *	½ period	Must be carried out first
2	None *	1 period	No. Can be done in any order
3	None *	1½ periods	
4	None *	1½ periods	
5	None *	4 periods	No
6	None	3 periods	No
7	Parental consent forms	2 periods	No
8		3 periods	Activity 7
9		2 periods	Activity 8
10 (1)	Consent forms	1 period, then hourly roadside recording throughout the day	No
10 (2)	Consent forms	4 periods	No
11	Consent forms	Hourly recording throughout the day	No

Assumes that apparatus for these Activities has already been made.

To be bought or obtained from other departments

Transformer to operate carts A and B (Fischer
  Technik)
Small model car with steerable front wheels
Long tape measure (100 m)

To be collected

Sand paper

Assumed normally available in laboratory

Small screwdriver
Adhesive tape
Retort stand
Plastic sheets
Metre rule
Chalk
Crushed ice
Oil
Washing up liquid
Plasticine
Graph paper
Stop watch

Notes for teacher

This Unit can be roughly divided into five
sections: (a) braking effects, (b) driving round
corners, (c) skidding, (d) speed and (e) traffic
flow and traffic heaviness. Each section can
be treated independently and therefore the
Activities could be arranged as a circus for
five groups of pupils. Since the majority of the
experiments provide results which must be
recorded with some attempt at interpretation,
it is important that the pupils thoroughly
understand the processes and procedures
involved before any attempt is made at group
work.

Activities 1-4 (braking effects)

These Activities are fairly straightforward,
provided the methods of (a) adjusting the
brake spring and (b) calculating averages are
understood. Other factors can be investigated;
e.g. effects of load on the truck, front versus
rear wheel braking, use of tread on tyres.

Activity 5 (driving round corners)

This Activity clearly illustrates the important
part that differentials play in vehicles

generally. The carts A and B are constructed
from Fischer Technik materials which are
easily made up from the suggested kit of parts
(see list on page 00). If oil is found to be a
little messy, washing up liquid can be
substituted. Other surfaces should also be
tried.

Note on differential

The differential unit allows the wheels on the
driven axle to turn at different speeds
although drive is still transmitted to both
wheels. This is necessary when cornering
where the wheel on the outside of the curve
has to travel a greater distance than that on
the inside of the curve.

The diff has a major disadvantage in
slippery conditions. If one driven wheel is on
ice, say, while the other is on tarmac, since
the wheel on ice can turn easily it 'absorbs' all
the drive from the engine at the expense of
the other wheel. The result is that the vehicle
does not move but the one wheel spins.
Tractors and overland vehicles have a diff lock
to inactivate the diff when negotiating slippery
terrain

Activity 6 (skidding)

Some reading with understanding is required
under the six headings 'What to do' (pages
12-14, pupils' book). Although the procedures
are not difficult, dialogue with the group may
be necessary. It is important that some
safeguard is used to prevent the car falling on
the floor. Since in reality the results of
skidding cause many accidents, the
observations made in this Activity should be
thoroughly discussed. This is a very important
section.

Activities 7-9 (speed)

Some help with the simple arithmetical
processes may be needed by some pupils. The
use of the graphs on pages 17, 18 and 21 of
the pupils' book may also need explanation.

Activities 10 and 11 (traffic flow and traffic heaviness)

The ideas covered in these two Activities are
easy; but discussion with the group(s)
collecting the data is important *before* they
are allowed on the road. Not all groups need
carry out these Activities. It may be sufficient

to use only one group which is reliable and well briefed, provided that the collected data is made available to other groups. The main difficulty will be organising the collection of information throughout the day.

Traffic heaviness is a measure of how close together cars are, but not of the number passing in a given time.

Main objectives and ideas

Main objectives
1. Awareness that several factors affect the results of braking
2. A knowledge of how the differential helps vehicles round corners and how it hinders traction in slippery conditions
3. Understanding of how speed is calculated
4. Awareness of the causes of skidding
5. Awareness of the meaning of traffic flow and traffic heaviness
6. An appreciation of the relationship between flow and heaviness

Key ideas
1. Speed, locked wheels and road surfaces are some of the factors which contribute to longer stopping distances
2. Differentials allow back wheels to rotate independently
3. Methods used to calculate speed
4. Use and interpretation of graphs
5. Main causes of skidding are harsh steering and harsh braking
6. Traffic flow is related to time of day. Traffic heaviness relates to time of day but also to type and condition of road

Relevant information
1. Various road safety films. See the catalogue of the Central Office of Information, Government Building, Bromyard Avenue, London W3, telephone 01-743 5555.
2. Roadcraft (H.M.S.O.)
3. Automobile Association *Book of the car* (1976)
4. Department of the Environment *Highway Code* (H.M.S.O.)

Information for each Activity

Activity 1:
Using the apparatus

Objective
Familiarisation with the working of the skid truck

Experience
Using the skid truck on a slope

Skills involved
1. Arranging the truck correctly on the sloping track
2. Observing what happens when it is released, particularly the action of the small and large wheels

Unfamiliar words
Plastic, slope, apparatus

Safety points
None

General notes
Allow the pupils sufficient time to become familiar with the truck and how to place it on the track. Some pupils may need help.

Apparatus list
Small screwdriver
Adhesive tape
Retort stand
Skid test truck
Track
Plastic sheet

Details for any construction
See the table on page 180 for a list of meccano parts needed to construct the skid test truck. See the diagram in the pupils' book for the construction.

See diagram 38, page 180, for construction of the track.

Activity 2:
Speed

Objective
Awareness that braking can lead to skidding

Experience
Using model skid truck and slope to find stopping distances

Skills involved
1. Arranging slope 20 cm and 40 cm above table
2. Correctly positioning truck on slope
3. Making observations
4. Measuring distances

Unfamiliar words
Opposite, usually, distance

Safety points
None

General notes
It may be necessary to discuss average distance and also the answer to the question before the pupils write their answers.

Apparatus list
Skid test truck
Track
Plastic sheet
Metre rule
Retort stand
Adhesive tape
Pencil
Chalk

Details for any construction
See Activity 1

Activity 3:
Wheel lock

Objective
Awareness of what happens to a vehicle when the wheels become locked

Experience
Releasing the skid truck down a slope to find

out what happens when the brakes are applied

Skills involved
1. All those for Activity 2
2. Using screwdriver to adjust braking bush

Unfamiliar words
Sensible, locked, adjusting bush, vehicle anti-locking devices, improve, important, travelled

Safety points
None

General notes
1. 'What to do' (4) may need some discussion.
2. It may be worth demonstrating how to adjust the brake bush.
3. Some pupils may need help with question 3.

Apparatus list
Skid test truck
Track
Plastic sheet
Small screwdriver
Metre rule
Retort stand
Adhesive tape
Pencil
Chalk

Details for any construction
See Activity 1

Activity 4:
Road surface

Objective
Awareness that different road surfaces affect stopping distances

Experience
Investigating stopping distances on different surfaces

Skills involved
1. All those for Activity 2
2. Using screwdriver to adjust braking bush
3. Changing the 'road surfaces' to be investigated

Unfamiliar words
Crushed, different, average, surface

Safety points
None

General notes
1. Some help may be needed with the arithmetic.
2. Truck wheels should be dried and oil removed between runs.

Apparatus list
Skid test truck
Track
Plastic sheet
Small screwdriver
Retort stand
Adhesive tape
Sand paper
Water
Oil
Crushed ice

Details for any construction
See Activity 1

Activity 5:
Driving round corners

Objective
To understand the importance of a differential in the driving axles of vehicles

Experience
Using model cars to investigate the advantage of differential gears

Skills involved
1. Care with handling carts A and B
2. Ability to move motor gears to engage axle gears
3. Ability to change motor from cart A to cart B
4. Making observations and recording these
5. Improvising a slope for carts to climb

Unfamiliar words
Slide, axle, differential, connect, straight, pointing, easily, climb

Safety points
The transformer used to operate the carts needs to be plugged into the mains supply. Check safety. (There is a useful transformer made by Fischer Technik.)

General notes
It may be useful to demonstrate how to transfer the motor from cart A to cart B and also how to move the front wheels to obtain directional change.

Apparatus list
Cart A
Cart B
Transformer (Fischer Technik) or power pack and leads
House brick
Board with plastic sheet attached
Small can of oil

Details for any construction
See the table on page 180 for a list of Fischer Technik parts needed to construct carts A and B.

See diagrams on page 8 of the pupils' book for the construction of the front parts of the carts. See diagram 39, page 180, for the construction of the rear wheel and support.

A strong bin liner can be used for the plastic sheet.

Activity 6:
What makes a car skid

Objective
Awareness that skidding while negotiating a corner leads to loss of directional control

Experience
Using a model car with steerable front wheels to investigate skidding when cornering

Skills involved
1. Securing plastic sheet in correct position on the table
2. Positioning table to give slope
3. Using plasticine to immobilise (a) front wheels and (b) rear wheels

Unfamiliar words
Plasticine, steering wheel, straight, sharply, arrowed line, curve, dangerous

Safety points
None

General notes
This Activity has six short experiments, each one needing slight re-adjustment to the steering or immobilisation of the wheels. Some dialogue and discussion may be needed during the practical work with some pupils. Since many accidents are caused by skidding, it may be worth allowing extra time to discuss the results and to relate these to the situation on the roads.

Apparatus list
Car with steerable front wheels
Plastic sheet
Washing up liquid
Plasticine
Adhesive tape

Details for any construction
None

Activity 7:
Walking and running

Objective
To understand the meaning of speed and the methods of its calculation

Experience
To find personal speeds for running and walking over a specified distance

Skills involved
1. Understanding simple numerical division
2. Measuring a specified distance
3. Using a stop watch
4. Using a simple speed/time graph and conversion graph

Unfamiliar words
Measurement, dividing (numbers), record, graph, curved line, travelled, convert, kilometres, abbreviations (km/h; m/s; mph)

Safety points
None

General notes
1. With some pupils it may be necessary to revise the method of numerical division.
2. The graphs on pages 17 and 18 may need some explanation before being used.
3. Discussion will be needed before pupils attempt question 3 of 'What to do: 2' (page 18 of pupils' book).

Apparatus list
Long metric tape measure
Chalk
Stop watch
Clip board (for pupil note taking)
Graph paper (some pupils only)

Details for any construction
None

Activity 8:
Finding the speed of a car

Objective
A knowledge of how the speed of cars is calculated

Experiences
Timing cars over a measured distance and using a graph to find the actual speed in mph

Skills involved
1. Measuring a specified distance (100 m)
2. Using a stop watch to time a car over this measured distance
3. Using a speed/time graph to complete 'speed' column on Traffic Speed Count sheet

Unfamiliar words
Decide, vehicle

Safety points
If pupils are out of school unaccompanied by a teacher the necessary safety regulation must be adhered to, i.e. by obtaining consent forms. Pupils must be thoroughly briefed on the method of carrying out this Activity.

General notes
Since this Activity depends on collecting and collating data and using conversion graphs, many pupils will need help.

Apparatus list
Long metric tape measure
Chalk
Stop watch
Clip board

Details for any construction
None

Activity 9:
(Further analysis of the results of Activity 8)

Objective
Collating, interpreting and displaying data

Experience
Processing data previously collected

Skills involved
1. Collecting data according to a given criterion
2. Using sets of results to produce a block graph

Unfamiliar words
Engineer, block graph, maximum, vehicle, sensible

Safety points
None

General notes
Some pupils may need a 'talk through' before attempting to construct the graphs. Interpretation of the graphs is needed to answer questions on page 24.

Apparatus list
None

Details for any construction
None

Activity 10:
Traffic heaviness

Objective
A knowledge of how traffic heaviness (density) is estimated

Experience
Using a measured distance along a road to calculate traffic heaviness

Skills involved
1. Measuring a specified distance along a road (*mark pavement only*)
2. Method of counting vehicles passing
3. Filling in forms correctly

Unfamiliar words
Heaviness, pavement, markers, immediately, complicated junction

Safety points
See 'Safety points' for Activity 8.

General notes
The main difficulty here is the organisation needed to collect the data required over such a long period. (See 'Notes for teacher'.)

Apparatus list
100 m tape measure (metric)
Clip board

Details for any construction
None

Activity 11:
Measuring traffic flow

Objective
Understanding the meaning of traffic flow

Experience
Finding the actual traffic flow on a given stretch of road

Skills involved
1. Method of counting vehicles passing a given point in one minute
2. Using a stop watch
3. Correct procedure for filling in form and plotting graph

Unfamiliar words
Understand, sensible, plot

Safety points
See 'Safety points' for Activity 8.

General notes
Discussion of the results obtained by the various groups is essential. It is also crucial to spend time on the interpretation of the data collected.

Apparatus list
Stop watch
Clip board

Details for any construction
None

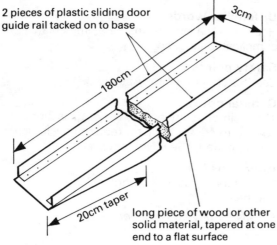

2 pieces of plastic sliding door guide rail tacked on to base

3cm

180cm

20cm taper

long piece of wood or other solid material, tapered at one end to a flat surface

DIAGRAM 38. Construction of the track (Activities 1-4).

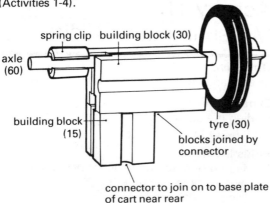

spring clip   building block (30)

axle
(60)

building block
(15)

tyre (30)

blocks joined by connector

connector to join on to base plate of cart near rear

DIAGRAM 39. Rear wheel and support for Fischer Technik carts A and B (Activity 5).

Meccano parts needed to construct the skid test truck used in Activities 1-4

Item	Part no	Size	Qty
Flanged plate	52	60 mm × 140 mm	1
Pulley	20a	50 mm diameter	2
Flange wheel	20b	19 mm diameter	4
Axle rod	16	90 mm	2
Axle rod	15	130 mm	1
Flat trunnion	126a	—	4
Collar with screw	59	—	7
Curved strip stepped	90a	60 mm	2
Girder bracket	161	—	1
Motor tyre*	142a	50 mm internal diameter, 70 mm external diameter	4
Double angle strip	48a	60 mm × 12 mm	1
Flexible plate	188	60 mm × 38 mm	1
Nut and bolt	37	—	24
Compression spring	— +	50 mm length	1

* Tyres will fit onto the pulleys although this is not the usually accepted practice. Four tyres are needed — two should be sanded flat, i.e. the tread should be removed.
+ The compression spring is not meccano but is part of the spring used for energy transfer experiments, Nuffield Combined Science no. 88.

Fischer Technik parts needed to construct carts A and B used in Activity 5

| Item | Part no | Quantities | |
		Cart A	Cart B
Base plate 180 × 90	4310011	1	1
Building blocks 30	3310031	5	5
Building blocks 15	3310051	2	2
Building blocks 15 with 2 round pegs	3310071	1	1
Spring clips	3310231	3	3
Differential gear box*	3310431	—	1
Axle 110	4310313	1	1
Axle 60	4310323	1	1
Connectors 15	4310601	3	3
Flat hubs	3310141	4	4
Tyres 45	3410181	2	2
Tyres 30	4310171	1	1
Gear wheel Z 20	4310211	1	1
Pinion with screw clamp Z10*	3310471	1	—
Mini-mot kit No 10	Art No 2/30201/5	1	1
Mini-mot kit No 11	Art No 2/30202/5	1	1
Rubber ring 37 × 2.5	4360517	2	2
Transformer 812 +	—		

* Since both carts A and B are constructed similarly except for those items marked * one cart may be sufficient if the 'differential' and 'pinion with screw clamp' could be changed over for the suggested Activities.
+ A battery unit is available.

Answers to questions in pupils' book

A letter D indicates that the answer cannot be predicted, usually because it is dependent on the results of the class experiments.

Activity 2
1. Yes. Faster vehicles need much greater distances to stop.

Activity 3
What to do
4. To get a more reliable (or average) result
5, 7. D
Questions
1. It stops quicker with them just turning, i.e. not locked on.
2. Because this would lock the wheels which is not the most effective way to stop
3. They stop the wheels from locking and so ensure greater stopping ability.
4. Because speed affects braking distance. We want to eliminate this factor while we investigate wheel lock.
5. **(a)** Clamp top of slope 40 cm above table.
   (b) Let go of the truck at the *top* of the slope.

Activity 4
1. Yes
2. Rough
3. Wet and oily

Activity 5
What to do: 1
3. also stops.
4. is still free to turn.
What to do: 2
5. No
6. Yes
7. Yes. Holding one stops both.
10. Yes.
11. Yes, the front one. The cart does not want to travel round the corner.
What to do: 3
3. Yes, at twice the speed; Faster
4. Both wheels turn together. The other one continues to turn, but faster.
5. Yes

6. The wheels do not slide. The truck goes round the corner easily.
What to do: 4
6. The wheel in the oil spun round and the truck did not climb the slope. All the 'rotation' went into the spinning wheel. Yes.
7. It climbed easily. Both wheels move together so if one has grip the vehicle has traction.
Questions
1. So that they can drive round corners easily with little tyre wear

Activity 6
What to do: 1
6. No; Yes; Yes; C
What to do: 2
2. Yes, slightly
What to do: 3
2. Yes, a lot; Back
What to do: 4
3. Yes; Yes; Yes;
What to do: 5
3. Yes
4.

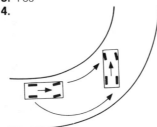

What to do: 6
3. No
4.

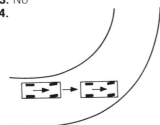

Questions
1. 4, 3, 2, 1
2. Water, Ice; Oil
3. Brakes; Steering
4. When going round a corner; this is most likely to cause a skid.
5. Vehicle does not go in desired direction because front wheels are used for steering. Very difficult to control.

Activity 7
How to use the graph
4. 2 m/s; 5 m/s
What to do: 2
1. 13.2; 17.8
2. 26.4; 31.2; 44

Activity 8
1-3 D

Activity 9
1. Graph 1
2. Graph 2
3. They are bunched together because there are more of them.
4-9 D

Activity 10
Questions: page 27
1-3 D
Questions: page 28
1. To avoid rush hour and to measure long periods of steady, 'typical' traffic
2. D

Activity 11
1, 2 D
3. Queues form.
4. Traffic heaviness is a measure of how close together vehicles are. Traffic flow is the number of vehicles which pass at a point in a given time interval.

Traffic flow and heaviness
2. Motorway and dual carriageway
4. Handle large traffic flows

Structures

Summary of contents

This Unit is very practical; it attempts to deal with the type of problems that might be encountered in everyday life. There is sufficient material for the pupil to find out what is needed to make a structure rigid. The idea of structure is introduced in the first few Activities. Pupils are given instructions on how to make cardboard girders and concrete beams. These models are then tested to destruction in order to find out how shape is important in the design of these kinds of structures. There are additional Activities which show how curing and reinforcing can give added strength to many kinds of structural material. Comparisons between the rigidity of rod and tube are also investigated.

The second part of the Unit deals with fixing things and gluing things. Glues, joints and rawlplugging are considered. In modern houses there are plasterboard walls; fixing things to these kinds of structures has not been forgotten.

Towards the end of the Unit some work is done on the properties of materials and their application.

Equipment list for whole of Unit

To be made
Saddles (P.V.C.) for cardboard girders (Activity 2)
Concrete beam mould (Activity 3)
Saddles (metal) for concrete beams (Activity 4)
Small strips of wood for gluing (Activities 12 and 14)
Plasterboard cavity wall model (Activity 18)

To be bought or obtained from other departments
Card (for girders)
Adhesives (several different makes)
Cement
Sand
Gravel
Aluminium rod
Aluminium tube } same dimensions
Boxes of Geo-strips or meccano
2 mm steel rod (steel welding rods can be used)
Rubber bands (thin and thick)
Nylon fishing line
Hand drills
Masonry drills (No 8 and No 10)
Breeze blocks
Rawlplugs (wooden and plastic types)
Screwdrivers
No 8 screws
Large cuphooks
Special plugs for cavity walls

To be collected
Plastic beakers
Odd pieces of wood (for mixing concrete and to protect floor from falling masses)
Pieces of dowel rod (for mixing concrete)
Polystyrene foam
String
P.V.C. sheet
Polythene film
Thick metal springs (as used in furniture)
Cotton thread

Assumed normally available in laboratory
Scissors
Metre rule
Half-metre rule
Several mass carriers
Several masses
Oil or grease
Safety screen
Safety goggles
Thick copper wire

Forward planner

Activity number	Advanced planning needed	Approximate Activity time (40 min period)	Are results of a previous Activity necessary?
1	Select suitable card. Cut into 50 cm wide sections (this is an easily manageable size for pupils to cut their own girders)	Double period	No
2	Make P.V.C. saddles	Double period	Activity 1
3	Make concrete beam moulds. Obtain sheets of polythene to cover benches and some suitable pieces of wood or dowel to mix concrete	2 or 3 double periods (depends if reinforcing is considered). Concrete needs to set before moulds can be used again	No
4	Make metal saddles. Prepare 'safety area' for testing beams. Obtain safety screen and goggles	Variable time (depends on how many beams are to be tested — particularly if a competition element has been introduced)	Activity 3
5	None	2 periods	No
6	Useful to collect photographs showing various structures	2 periods	No
7	None	1 period	No
8	None	1 period	No
9	Make sure that all the materials suggested are available (others may also be included)	2 periods	No
10 and 11	Test rubber bands	3 periods (1 double and 1 single)	No
12	Cut a large number of strips of wood — approx 15 mm wide × 8 cm long (it is important that all pieces of wood are the *same* size otherwise too many variables will be introduced)	Variable time (depends on number of joints prepared and tested) but allow approx 1 double period for each Activity	No
13			Activity 12
14			No
15			Activity 14
16	Make sure that sufficient hand drills and breeze blocks are available	2 periods	No
17	None	2 periods	Activity 16
18	Make a few plasterboard cavity wall models	2 periods	No
Quiz	None	1 period	Activities 16, 17 and 18

Bunsen burner
Heat resistant mat
Stands with clamp and boss head
Metal tongs
Aluminium foil

Bare copper wire (assorted sizes)
Metal springs
Rubber cord and rubber bands — varying sizes
G-clamps (also called G-cramps)

Notes for teacher

Since the suggested Activities in the Unit cover many of the 'Do it yourself' tasks carried out in most homes from time to time, there are many ways in which the Activities could be developed and extended into more detailed scientific investigations.

Use could also be made of the wide range of commercially produced constructional kits which could help to reinforce the idea of rigid structures. Again project work could be encouraged, e.g. build a cardboard bridge with a 50 cm span to carry a predetermined load.

There is also a strong link with photography. A photographic record of structures could be made, including buildings, bridges, visits to places where there is some connection with the construction industry and, of course, biological structures.

Activities 1 and 2

Before these Activities are attempted by pupils they should be tried out first by the teacher or under the teacher's direct supervision to find the most suitable card to use. Care is needed in supporting the girders for testing.

Before the girders are tested, the following points should be discussed:
1. How much of the girder should rest on the stool? (Once decided, this should remain constant.)
2. What is the area of contact between the saddle and the girder and where on the girder should the saddle be placed?
3. Does the use of different adhesives make any difference to the ultimate results?

Make sure there are sufficient pots of glue for pupils to work without having to wait for it.

Activities 3 and 4

Some thought is needed when organising these Activities. It is difficult to give the exact quantities of cement, sand and gravel needed because this obviously depends on how many beams are made. Again, as for girders, it might be useful for the teacher to actually make a few beams since this would give some idea of the quantities needed by each group.

Sheets of polythene are useful for covering the benches and old bowls and odd flat pieces of wood are useful for mixing purposes.

For the concrete mixture the aggregate needs to be small — aquarium gravel is about the right size.

It is important that enough moulds are available. In initial trials, it was found that tomato boxes with pieces of wood placed lengthwise down the box as dividers made very satisfactory moulds.

It is worthwhile covering the surface of the mould with a smear of grease (vaseline); this makes it easier to remove the beam from the mould when set. It is advisable to leave the concrete mix in the mould for at least two days. The beam must be removed with care (a table knife may help) and then left for several days to thoroughly dry.

Testing the beams will also need careful organisation. An area of the laboratory should be set aside for this purpose. Safety should be given a high priority. A bucket of sand under the saddle helps to cushion the impact of falling masses when the beam finally breaks.

Activity 5

Considerations similar to those in Activites 2 and 4 are needed here, regarding the distance between the stools and hence the amount of rod or tube resting on the stools. It is also important that both tube and rod have the same dimensions, and that zero on the rule is level with the tube or rod when no load is attached.

Activity 6

Geo-strips can be used instead of meccano strips. These are made from plastic and are therefore not so robust as the metal meccano parts, but they are much cheaper.

If neither of these are available some pupils could construct models of towers or bridges to show how they are kept rigid.

Some help may be needed with the names of the shapes on page 15 of the pupils' book.

Activity 7

Some discussion on metal fatigue would be appropriate here. It may also be worthwhile to refer to the 'Science 5/13' units 'Metals' and 'Metals: background information'

Activities 9-11

Some help may be needed here in filling in the table of results on page 19 of the pupils' book.

Rubber bands exhibit an interesting behaviour when stretched. The same type and dimension of band should be used if class results are to be compared, but investigations into the stretchability of other types of rubber bands can be carried out later by individual groups. Careful measurements will be required here and it may be wise to revise the skills needed to carry out these measurements.

A demonstration experiment could be set up to show an important property of some materials — creep. Since readings would be needed every 10 min it may be convenient to fit this in during a one period lesson and to use the interval time to summarise the results of the three Activities on stretching.

Activites 12-15

Here again many variables are involved:
1. The kind of wood used
2. The area of the joint
3. The length of leverage when testing
4. The adhesive used

These points must be discussed before the Activities are attempted.

It is important that pupils follow the manufacturers' instructions otherwise comparisons will not be fair when testing the adhesive properties of the glues. Safety precautions must be taken, e.g. the wearing of safety goggles.

Pupils should be encouraged to compare prices of glues as well as performance.

Activities 16-18

It is anticipated that pupils will discover for themselves that drilling into brick or cement blocks should be done slowly otherwise crumbling tends to make the plugging more difficult. Drilling with an electric drill requires a different skill to that needed for a hand drill. Electric drills tend to develop a 'will' of their own. However, the use of the electric drill for this purpose could be demonstrated.

Note: It is advisable not to use rawlplugging wool in schools. Nor is it necessary.

When drilling plasterboard extra care is needed. The model should be securely clamped and slowly drilled.

Rawlplug quiz

It is important to take a reasonable time over the quiz and to discuss the relevant points which should emerge.

Main objectives and ideas

Main objectives

1. Awareness that shape is also an important consideration in the design of structures
2. Understanding of how structures can be improved
3. Knowledge that bonding with adhesives assists the strength of structures in certain materials
4. Appreciation that wall structures must be considered before things are fixed to them
5. Awareness that before drilling walls in houses, certain precautions must be taken regarding safety

Key ideas

1. Girders are made in different shapes depending on the stresses that may be involved in the structure.
2. Concrete can be made in different 'mixes' depending on the strength required.
3. Modern adhesives can be used to make extremely rigid joints in many kinds of material.
4. Plugs used for wall fixing should be carefully selected depending on the 'weight' to be held and the kind of wall to which it is to be fixed.
5. An understanding of science outside the laboratory is needed in the day to day jobs needed to be done in and about the home.

Relevant information

A selection of good and easy to follow 'Do it yourself' books and magazines

Information for each Activity

Activity 1:
Making girders

Objective
Awareness that there are many forms of girders

Experience
To make various types of cardboard girders and test their structural properties

Skills involved
1. To measure and cut given lengths of card
2. To carry out specific written instructions for the process of constructing girders

Unfamiliar words
Girder

Safety points
None

General notes
It may be worthwhile to allow different groups to use different adhesives. This could introduce another variable which could be discussed.

Apparatus list
Sufficient quantity of card cut into 50 cm sections
Scissors
Glue (possibly two or three varieties)
Half-metre rule

Details for any construction
None

Activity 2:
Testing your girders

Objective
Knowledge that the strength of a girder is a function of its shape

Experience
To show that differences in the shapes of girders affect their load carrying capacity

Skills involved
1. Correctly arranging girders on stools in preparation for testing
2. Correct positioning of saddle and load
3. Observing what takes place and recording a result

Unfamiliar words
Saddle, breaking point, support

Safety points
Some provision should be made to catch the masses when the girder gives way. A bowl or bucket with sand in it would be useful here.

General notes
1. A pre-lesson talk to all groups will be needed here regarding the positioning of the girders on the stools. There must be an agreed length of girder resting on the supports.
2. This is a good chance to produce a photographic record of the girders, before and after testing.

Apparatus list
Stools
Mass carrier and masses
Saddle (plastic)
Cardboard girders made in Activity 1

Details for any construction
The plastic saddles can be made from strips of P.V.C. or acetate sheet about 3 cm wide and 20 cm long. They are folded and stapled as shown in diagram 40, page 195.

Activity 3:
Making concrete beams

Objective
Knowledge of how concrete is made

Experience
Making concrete beams using cement, sand and gravel in varying amounts

Skills involved
1. Preparing the mould

2. Preparing and mixing the cement, sand and gravel in the suggested proportions
3. Transferring the mix to the mould and completing the preparation of the beam according to suggested instructions

Unfamiliar words
Concrete, mould, grease, reinforce, gauze

Safety points
Care must be taken with cement — avoid getting the dust in the eyes.

General notes
1. Grease the mould before adding concrete.
2. Make sure that beams made from different mixes are clearly marked.
3. If pupils are interested, this Activity can be extended to cover curing of concrete, the effect of old cement, etc.

Apparatus list
Concrete beam mould
Cement
Dry sand
Gravel
Measuring cup (plastic beaker)
Mixing board
Wooden mixing 'spoon'
Water (in suitable containers)
Grease

Details for any construction
See diagram 41, page 195 for construction of the concrete beam mould.

Activity 4:
Testing concrete beams

Objective
Ability to carry out tests according to given criteria

Experience
Finding out which concrete mix gives the best results

Skills involved
1. Positioning beam on stools
2. Arranging saddle for carrying loads
3. Recognising and carrying out the necessary safety precautions

4. Observing and recording results

Unfamiliar words
Saddle, support, protect

Safety points
1. Goggles must be worn — there is always the danger that when concrete breaks up, small pieces may fly into the air.
2. Arrange a suitable container half filled with sand or polystyrene foam to help break the fall of the masses when the beam finally gives way.

General notes
Safety problems can be kept to a minimum if a specialised area of the laboratory is set aside for these tests. The whole class can then watch each beam being tested.

Apparatus list
Concrete beams made in Activity 3
Stools
Metal saddle
Safety screens
Mass carrier and adequate supply of masses
Odd piece of thick wood or sand in containers
Safety goggles

Details for any construction
The metal saddle can be made from any strip of metal about 1 cm wide bent twice through 90° to fit round the beam. A piece of meccano is ideal for this. A thin metal rod passing through holes in the ends of the strip completes the fourth side of the rectangle and the masses are hung from this.

Activity 5:
Rigidity of aluminium tubing

Objective
Awareness that tubular structures possess properties of rigidity similar to those made from solid material

Experience
Comparing the strengths of aluminium tube and aluminium rod of the same dimensions

Skills involved

1. Arranging tubing and rod on stools
2. Correct positioning of mass carrier
3. Measuring amount of bend in both rod and tube
4. Observing and recording results

Unfamiliar words

Aluminium, metre, hollow, repeat

Safety points

G-clamps placed either side of the rod and tube would prevent these falling to the ground when loaded.

General notes

1. It is most important that the rod and tube are of the same dimensions.
2. Sufficient readings can be taken without permanently deforming the rod or tube.

Apparatus list

Aluminium rod
Aluminium tube } same diameter and same length (about 3 mm diameter and ½-1 m long are suitable dimensions)

Mass carrier and masses
Stand with boss head and clamp
Half-metre rule

Details for any construction
None

Activity 6:
Rigid structures

Objective

Knowledge that certain shapes are necessary in the design of rigid structures

Experience

Using plastic or metal strips to make rigid shapes

Skills involved

1. Choosing the correct length of strip for the construction of a particular shape
2. Fixing the strips together
3. Testing the rigidity of the shape
4. Observing and tabulating results

Unfamiliar words

Rigid, collapse

Safety points

None

General notes

Some help may be needed with the names of shapes and their identification. A display of photographs showing various structures would be useful here.

Apparatus list

Geo-strips (obtainable from suppliers of mathematics equipment to primary schools) and paper fasteners
OR
Meccano strips (borrowed temporarily from pupils) with nuts and bolts

Details for any construction
None

Activity 7:
Altering copper wire

Objective

Knowledge that some of the physical properties of metals can be changed by mechanical means

Experience

Hardening copper wire by bending

Skills involved

1. Fixing wire to clamp and finding the maximum mass that it will support
2. Heating wire around its middle point in a bunsen flame
3. Work hardening the copper by bending it

Unfamiliar words

Strength, aeroplane, vibration, hardened

Safety points

Care is needed when holding the lighted bunsen in the hand to heat the copper wire.

General notes

A talk and discussion on metal fatigue may be useful here (see suggestion in 'Notes for teacher').

Apparatus list
Thick copper wire (about 20 cm lengths)
Bunsen burner
Stand with boss head and clamp
Heat resistant mat
Small pieces of wood (to help support the
  wire in the clamp)
Pair of pliers (for bending wire)
100 g mass
Tongs

Details for any construction
None

Apparatus list
Pieces of steel rod about 3 mm in diameter
  and 5 or 6 cm long (steel welding rods are
  useful for this purpose)
Beaker
Tongs
Bunsen burner
Heat resistant mat
Safety goggles

Details for any construction
None

Activity 8:
Heat treatment of steel rod

Objective
Knowledge that some of the physical
properties of metals can be changed by
mechanical means

Experience
Hardening steel rod by heat treatment

Skills involved
1. Heating steel rod in bunsen flame
2. Taking care in the method of quenching,
   especially if glass beakers are used
3. Ability to carry out tests and to observe
   possible changes

Unfamiliar words
Quenching, impossible, brittle, treatment

Safety points
Care is needed (a) when holding the steel rod
in the flame and (b) when transferring it to the
beaker containing cold water — there will be a
violent reaction when the red hot steel meets
the cold water.

General notes
There are many films and filmstrips available
from the Film Library of the British Steel
Corporation which may be appropriate to
show here. Apply to the Corporation at
12 Addiscombe Road, Croydon, Surrey,
telephone 01-686 0366.

Activity 9:
Changing the shape of materials

Objective
Awareness that some materials when under a
stress may become permanently deformed

Experience
Using a collection of materials to find out how
stress may affect their shape

Skills involved
1. Selecting named materials
2. Testing materials by pressing and pulling
3. Observing and collating results and
   entering them in a table

Unfamiliar words
Behave, polystyrene, polythene, nylon, spring
balance, wrapping

Safety points
Some care is needed when rubber and other
springy materials are under tension. Sudden
release may cause an accident.

General notes
Although the actual testing of the material is
fairly straightforward, some pupils may need
guidance in filling in the table of results.

Apparatus list
Collection of different materials — e.g.
  Polystyrene foam
  String
  Rubber cord
  Polythene film

189

Aluminium foil
Thin and thick copper wire
Thin and thick rubber bands
Nylon fishing line
Thin and thick metal springs

Details for any construction
None

Activity 10:
Stretching rubber bands

Objective
An understanding of the behaviour of materials when under stress

Experience
Using rubber bands to simulate the action of a simple spring balance

Skills involved
1. Setting up the apparatus
2. Measuring the amount of stretch
3. Entering the results correctly in the table provided
4. Using results to estimate the mass of other objects
5. Drawing a graph (not essential, but useful if time allows)

Unfamiliar words
Weighing machine, spring balance

Safety points
None

General notes
1. The ruler for measuring the stretch should be secured in another clamp or slotted base.
2. The stand supporting the rubber band would be more secure if held on the bench by a G-clamp.

Apparatus list
Rubber band
1 stand complete with boss head and clamp
1 rod from another stand (to suspend rubber band and weights from)
Half-metre rule
Mass carrier and masses (up to 300 g)

Details for any construction
None

Activity 11:
Stretching rubber bands further

Objective
An understanding of the behaviour of materials when under stress

Experience
Stretching rubber bands beyond their elastic limit

Skills involved
1. Setting up the apparatus
2. Taking measurement readings of the amount of stretch and noting the masses used
3. Entering results in tabular form
4. Interpreting results in order to answer questions

Unfamiliar words
Loading readings, unloading readings

Safety points
1. Depending upon the type and quality of the rubber bands, the rubber may become so deformed under stress that it will break. Some receptacle containing sand would be useful to contain the falling masses.
2. Since close observation is needed and there is the possibility that the rubber may break, goggles should be worn.

General notes
Before questions are attempted, group and class results should be carefully and thoroughly discussed.

Apparatus list
Rubber bands (same type as used in Activity 10)
1 stand with boss head and clamp
1 rod from another stand
Half-metre rule
Mass carrier and masses (up to 700 g)
Safety goggles

Details for any construction
None

Activity 12:
Which glue is best?

Objective
Ability to carry out simple investigations based on a set of suggested criteria

Experience
To investigate the adhesive nature of a selection of glues on simple wooden joints

Skills involved
1. Ability to select and name adhesive
2. Measuring area to be glued
3. Applying glue correctly
4. Reading instructions on packets

Unfamiliar words
Names of adhesives (Bostick, UHU, Evo-stick, etc.), impact, instructions

Safety points
Discourage glue sniffing.

General notes
1. Impress upon pupils the importance of following the manufacturers' instructions. If some pupils have difficulty with language, the instructions must be explained to them.
2. Glue sniffing can be dangerous — a discussion on this may be worthwhile during this lesson.
3. Several glued joints can be put into the same G-clamp.

Apparatus list
Small strips of wood (each group will need at least 10), dimensions are not important but they all must be the same, e.g. 8 cm × 2 cm × 0.5 cm
G-clamp
A selection of adhesives (e.g. Evo-stick impact, Dunlop Thixofix, Bostik clear, UHU, carpentry glue)

Details for any construction
None

Activity 13:
Testing the glues

Objective
Ability to carry out simple investigations based on a set of suggested criteria

Experience
Testing wooden joints which have been glued together using different adhesives

Skills involved
1. Setting up the apparatus for testing the joints
2. Recognition of variables involved:
   (a) clamping distance on bench
   (b) mass distance from joints
   (c) position of joint
3. Observing and recording information

Unfamiliar words
Strongest, weakest, load

Safety points
1. Goggles must be worn.
2. Arrange some receptacle to catch falling masses.

General notes
1. It is important that pupils realise the number of variables involved. These should be discussed thoroughly before the testing begins.
2. It should be emphasised that the wood sometimes breaks rather than the glue giving way. Discussion is needed on how this could be recorded.

Apparatus list
G-clamp
Mass carrier and masses
String
Prepared joints (from Activity 12)
Stool
Suitable receptacle for catching masses when joint breaks
Safety goggles

Details for any construction
None

Activity 14:
Area of joint

Objective
Ability to carry out simple investigations based on a set of suggested criteria

Experience
Gluing together pieces of wood using the same adhesive, but over different areas

Skills involved
1. Measuring and marking pieces of wood to indicate suggested areas for the application of the glue
2. Putting the corresponding areas together correctly
3. Clamping the joints together

Unfamiliar words
Shaded area

Safety points
Discourage glue sniffing.

General notes
See 'General notes' for Activity 12.

Apparatus list
Several small strips of wood, all the same size (approx dimensions 8 cm × 2 cm × 0.5 cm)
G-clamp
One particular type of glue for all groups (e.g. UHU)

Details for any construction
None

Activity 15:
Testing the joints

Objective
Ability to carry out simple investigations based on a set of suggested criteria

Experience
Testing wooden joints which have been glued together with the same adhesive, but over different areas

Skills involved
See 'Skills involved' for Activity 13.

Unfamiliar words
None

Safety points
See 'Safety points' for Activity 13.

General notes
See 'General notes' for Activity 13. Results obtained here and those obtained from Activity 13 should be compared, but only with those using the same type of adhesive.

Apparatus list
Prepared wooden joints (from Activity 14)
G-clamp
Mass carrier and masses
String
Suitable receptacle for catching masses when joint breaks

Details for any construction
None

Activity 16:
Rawlplugging

Objective
An understanding of the methods that can be used to support various objects, e.g. shelves and cupboards, on a variety of different wall structures

Experience
Drilling and plugging a breeze block

Skills involved
1. Correct use of drill — holding it at 90° to the material being drilled, drilling slowly and never using excessive pressure on the drill
2. Comparing depth of penetration with type of plug being used
3. Inserting plug by gentle tapping

Unfamiliar words
Masonry drill bit, rawlplug, breeze block

Safety points
1. Care must be taken when drilling — correct procedures must be followed.
2. Breeze blocks must be held while drilling is taking place. The pupil holding the block should wear safety goggles.

General notes
1. Drilling would be better carried out on the floor rather than on a bench.
2. Cover the floor with newspapers — plastic sheet tends to slip.
3. It is important that pupils know the correct way to operate the drill (see 'Notes for teacher' regarding use of electric drill).

Apparatus list
Hand drill
Breeze block (or parts of breeze block)
No 8 masonry drill bit
Plastic rawlplugs (No 8)
Wooden (fibre) rawlplugs (No 8)
Screwdriver (medium size)
No 8 screws
Safety goggles
Newspapers

Details for any construction
None

Activity 17:
Testing rawlplugs

Objective
An understanding of the methods that can be used to support various objects, e.g. shelves and cupboards, on a variety of different wall structures

Experience
Testing the strengths of wood and plastic rawlplugs

Skills involved
1. See 'Skills involved' for Activity 16.
2. Correctly setting up breeze block on stool supports

Unfamiliar words
None

Safety points
1. The breeze block must be correctly supported on the stools.
2. There must be some provision to catch falling masses.

General notes
It is important to discuss the use and function

of both types of rawlplug — many things fixed to walls are not heavy.

Apparatus list
Hand drill
Breeze block
Masonry drill bit
Rawlplugs — plastic and wooden (fibre)
2 large cuphooks
Mass carrier and masses
2 stools
Some protection for floor (wood or suitable receptacle and sand)

Details for any construction
None

Activity 18:
Fixing in plasterboard walls

Objective
An understanding of the methods that can be used to support various objects, e.g. shelves and cupboards, on a variety of different wall structures

Experience
Drilling and fixing objects to plasterboard walls using cavity wall model

Skills involved
1. Correct method of holding drill (less pressure needed)
2. Understanding how the special rawlplug works
3. Inserting special rawlplugs

Unfamiliar words
Plasterboard, special, cavity

Safety points
The cavity wall model should be clamped to bench before drilling is started.

General notes
It may be worthwhile to discuss with the groups how one can find out whether a wall is solid or whether it is plasterboard with a cavity between adjacent walls.

Apparatus list
Plasterboard cavity wall model
Hand drill
No 10 masonry drill bit
7/16'' masonry drill bit
Plastic rawlplug
Special rawlplug for cavity walls

Screws
Screwdriver

Details for any construction
See diagram 42, page 196 for construction of
the plasterboard cavity wall model.

Answers to questions in pupils' book

A letter D indicates that the answer cannot be
predicted, usually because it is dependent on
the results of the class experiments.

Activity 4
1. The reinforced one
2, 3. D

Activity 5
1. Tubing, but not a great deal more
2. Rod
3. It is lighter.
4. Climbing frames, scaffolding, metal framed polythene greenhouses, television aerials, some tennis rackets, some modern chairs, some handles of cooking pots

Activity 6
What to do
3. The triangle
5. Bicycle frame, bridge, gate, pylon, stool, tents, tripods

Activity 7
What to do
5. It is unable to support the mass.
7. Yes

Activity 8
What to do
1. No (may flex slightly); No; No

5. No; Yes
6. It needs to be very hard so it can cut through materials.
7. They are very brittle if you are not careful, particularly with thin drills.

Activity 9
1. Rubber perishes; a spring extends linearly.
2. It is transparent, clean, cheap, and clings after stretching.

Activity 10
What to do: 1
4. Ruler readings in table should increase and decrease in uniform steps
6. Yes; Yes

Activity 11
1. Yes, for lower readings
2, 3. D
4. They lose elasticity.
5. The band will break.
6. It may perish.
7. It would weaken the tyre so a slight bump or knock as you are driving along could cause a puncture. This could lead to an accident.

Activity 13
1-3 D

Activity 15
1. 5 and 6
2. Stronger

Activity 16
1. D
2. Plastic
3. D

Activity 18
What to do
3. Not firmly; Not heavy things
5. Yes; Yes; Special one
Rawlplug Quiz
1.
2. } Plastic or wood, not special
3. Special rawlplug
4. Plasterboard
5. It would not be strong enough to hold the weight.
6. They can work loose.
7. Above or below sockets and switches, above gas fire, above or below wall lights.

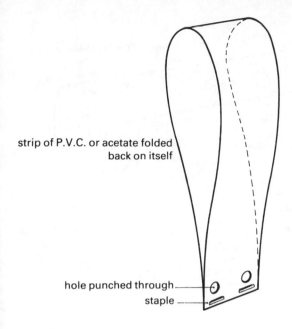

strip of P.V.C. or acetate folded
back on itself

hole punched through

staple

DIAGRAM 40. To make the plastic saddle
(Activity 2).

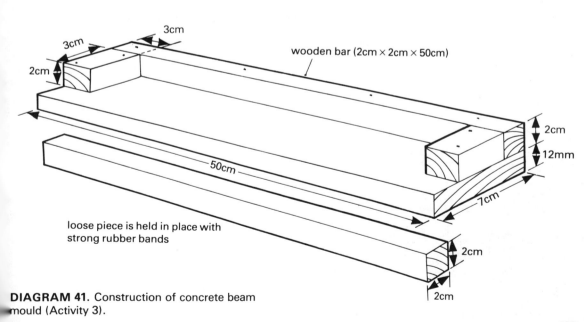

3cm

3cm

2cm

wooden bar (2cm × 2cm × 50cm)

2cm

12mm

50cm

7cm

loose piece is held in place with
strong rubber bands

2cm

DIAGRAM 41. Construction of concrete beam
mould (Activity 3).

2cm

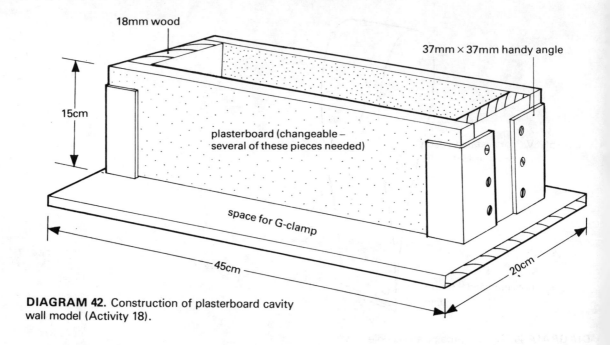

DIAGRAM 42. Construction of plasterboard cavity
wall model (Activity 18).